Praise for THE CURE FOR HEALTHCARE

"To fix the broken American healthcare system, one must truly understand how we broke it. This book is an important read for those seeking to understand the problem. In his book, Dr. Dale does an excellent deep dive into the problems in American medicine. He effectively describes the inherent problem with the failed federal policies and intrusive middlemen in healthcare. He takes readers on a complete journey by highlighting real-world functioning patient-centered solutions that removes barriers between doctors and patients."

—*Dr. Lee Gross, Co-founder and Senior Vice President of Epiphany Health and President, Docs4PatientCare Foundation*

"We live in an age where health insurance is unimaginably expensive. Yet, given skyrocketing deductibles, it is almost unusable for the average American. *The Cure for Healthcare* is a must-read for anyone who wants to actually fix the system and put the patient and his or her physician back at the center of American healthcare."

—*Dr. C.L. Gray, President, Physicians for Reform*

"To read this book is to become better acquainted with Dr. Tony Dale, a man I'm honored to call a friend and someone the medical free market revolution can also call a friend and co-combatant. Dr. Dale exemplifies Ortega y Gasset's 'select man,' emboldened by challenges and unafraid to set new goals, the achievement of which benefit us all. Unwilling to rest on his many laurels, Dr. Dale has generously chosen to provide this guidebook meant to steer us clear from the gulag of the collectivist brand of medical 'care.'"

—*Dr. Keith Smith, Founder, Surgery Center for Oklahoma*

"When the history of the revolution to change the existing U.S. health-care system is written, there is no question that Dr. Tony Dale, a British immigrant doctor, will be named among the top original thinkers who began that revolution to transform the United States system of 'sick care' into one of 'healthcare.' By telling his own story, Dr. Dale thoughtfully explains the elements that allow for transformation of a system that over 90% of the U.S. population believes needs to be changed. Dr. Dale describes his journey from his 1987 arrival in Austin, Texas, through to his founding of Sedera, a leading medical cost sharing organization. He fosters a belief in American ingenuity that pushes us toward building the next generation of healthcare based on the free-market ecosystem. If you want to understand this revolution that has already begun, then read this book and act on it."

—*Dr. Firouz Daneshgari, Founder, BowTie Medical*

THE
CURE
FOR
HEALTHCARE

An Old World Doctor's
Prescription for the
New World Health System

DR. TONY DALE
Founder of Sedera

ISBN: 978-0-9892111-2-3 (print)

Printed in the United States of America on acid-free paper

10 9 8 7 6 5 4 3 2 1

First Edition

TO FELICITY

It was September 1968 when we met in London. We were both young, idealistic, and looking to change the world. I am not sure how much of that we have done. But after 50 years together, as partners in every sense of the word, I know I could not have written this book if Felicity had not been my strongest supporter and my strongest critic. When your wife is clearly a better doctor than you are, you have to find something else to boost your male ego. I tried table tennis, but she has now caught me up on that. I wrote some books in England, but she has more than overtaken me on the writing side since those days. Business: Even there, the ideas have always been hers, even if she is also smart enough to make sure that I then have to do most of the work. As the good book says, "He who finds a wife finds a good thing." I guess I found the best!

CONTENTS

FOREWORD

by Peter H. Diamandis, MD

Founder and Executive Chairman of the XPRIZE Foundation

THE BIGGER THE CHALLENGE, THE BOLDER and more inventive our approach must be. Having written extensively about the transformative power of 10X thinking when pursuing a Moonshot, I am delighted to have the opportunity to help unpack what Dr. Tony Dale compels us all to consider in his newest book, *The Cure for Healthcare.*

American healthcare has dominated newspaper headlines, political dialogue, and U.S. consumer spending for the past 15 years. But public conversation surrounding healthcare has generated far more heat than light. As a nation, we find ourselves grappling with the same challenges of unequal access, staggering costs, and tremendous variations in care quality from one part of the country—or even different parts of the same city—to another. The answer seems unlikely to involve pouring yet more money into a broken system, one that drives more spending than does any other national healthcare system on the planet. So how do we achieve this Moonshot of democratized, preventive, and continuously improving care?

Dr. Dale draws from his extensive background in medicine, from early exposure to healthcare as the child of a physician, to his own career as a family doctor, and his later founding of the Karis Group to assist patients with healthcare navigation and bill negotiation.

In this book, Dr. Dale unveils many of the extraordinary innovations now being birthed by physicians, among others, who understand that the answers to contemporary healthcare challenges can be found by returning to the basics. The word "radical" thereby entails "going back to the roots."

In alignment with this theme, the stories illustrated in this book take us back to the foundation of medical care, anchored in the doctor-patient relationship. Primary care doctors, by transitioning to a subscription-based model that costs less than most gym memberships, can provide outstanding 24/7 service to their patients. Radiologists, by offering completely open, transparent pricing—i.e. not dependent upon complex insurance relationships and esoteric policies—are cutting patient imaging costs in half. Surgeons, by moving away from third-party payment models, and instead offering cash-based alternatives that cover the whole surgical incident, can now eliminate the complexity of piecemeal charges (by each doctor, lab or facility involved). Not only does this type of surgical center provide far better care, but it does so at a fraction of the cost.

When we strive to transform something as complex as today's American healthcare system, the answer is likely found in greater simplicity. Pricing transparency and the re-establishment of a direct doctor-patient relationship can bring us far closer to our goal. *The Cure for Healthcare* offers us a novel roadmap to easier access, better outcomes, and lower costs. It also serves to highlight an unexpected yet remarkably effective shortcut to the finish line. Through Dr. Dale's compelling narrative, we learn that the key to transformation not only entails better medical technology and more insightful policies, but also the self-propelling power of the free market. When concerned business leaders shape the market by directing their spending on healthcare through physicians and facilities that focus on direct and cash pay models, everything changes. As I often expound in relation to other industries, by removing healthcare's myriad layers of middlemen—whether in the form of insurance companies, pharmacy benefit managers, government mandates and regulations, and beyond—the free market enables an environment wherein the 'cream' rises to the top. Basic principles of supply and demand thereby drive down costs and witness a surge in care quality and innovation. As Dr. Dale so deftly illustrates, this principle is increasingly apparent across the country as care providers make the transition to greater simplicity.

Every one of us shares the power and responsibility to transform the future of healthcare. This book offers us a practical blueprint to join the movement and give way to an abundant, efficient and innovative American healthcare system for all.

Peter H. Diamandis, MD
Santa Monica, CA

PREFACE

WHEN I ARRIVED IN THE UNITED STATES 33 years ago, I had no idea that I would become involved in the world of medical economics. I am a very ordinary family doctor who fell into this by accident. Unfortunately, the accident was to me!

Trying to keep up with my then teenage kids on the basketball court in 1996, I tore my medial meniscus (part of the cushioning in the knee) and needed to have it surgically repaired. Being a physician, I knew this was relatively minor surgery. However, I asked the surgeon what it was going to cost, because I was a recent immigrant from the UK, where all medical care is automatically paid for through our taxes. Here in the United States, I was going to be a self-paying patient. The surgeon told me it would cost about $2,000 to put right, which sounded reasonable to me. This was my introduction to the futility of the blind leading the blind—as Jesus put it in one of his famous sayings—within the medical economic context. Oh yes, and the end of that saying continues, "then they will both fall into the ditch."

Whether the orthopedic surgeon and I were blind or just plain ignorant, the end result was the same: My bills came to just under $15,000

($35,000 in today's dollars) for a 30-minute procedure that had me in the hospital at 6:30 in the morning and out four hours later. I guess you could say that the surgery was completely successful by any medical standard. But what about the significant financial damage done to me in the process? Does no one carry any responsibility for that?

Thus began my journey into the strange world of American medical economics. This industry, possibly the largest industry in the nation outside of the government itself, sucks up approximately one out of every five dollars spent within the national economy, but hardly anyone is satisfied with the results. Doctors are burning out at an alarming rate. Patient satisfaction surveys show dismally low scores. Between 1975 and 2010, the number of doctors in the U.S. grew by approximately 150 percent, while during the same time frame, the number of administrators within the healthcare ecosystem grew by approximately 3,200 percent. That is 20 times the growth of administrators to physicians over a 35-year period while health costs have escalated exponentially.[1]

Healthcare administrators far outpace physicians in growth

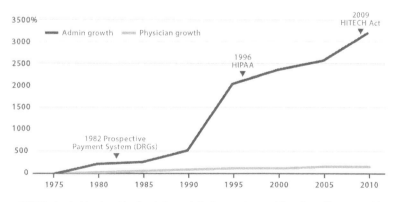

SOURCE: athenahealth analysis of data from the Bureau of Labor Statistics, the National Center for Health Statistics, and the United States Census Bureau's Current Population Survey

Fundamental changes in how medicine is practiced have occurred during this time frame. The role of government regulation, the movement from solo practice to larger group medical practices, and the rise of administrators have all combined to create the perfect environment for healthcare to become big business rather than a system primarily for the delivery of health and wellness to the patient. What needs to change to rectify this?

That is the fundamental question that I explore in this book. There are excellent books already available, such as Dr. Marty Makary's *The Price We Pay,* that explore what has gone wrong with the system. In this book, I have chosen to focus on changes that are spontaneously happening to put the process right. Doctors and patients, acting in ways that naturally bring common sense to the medical system, are exploring—and finding—many exciting ways to change the system for the better. Amidst the massive insurance companies, the stifling regulations, the layers upon layers of administrators, and the voracious greed of the medical industrial complex, an amazingly peaceful revolution is taking place. This revolution is putting the doctor–patient relationship back at the center of medicine. It is demonstrating that you can dramatically lower prices while enhancing the medical encounter for both patient and doctor and, in the process, significantly improve outcomes. What is not to like about such a revolution?

I am not an academic. Medical school was an enjoyable experience but what I really loved was my patients. I came to know them over the years, and there was something very rewarding about the way they came to know and appreciate my skills as a doctor. But it never occurred to me when I injured my knee and challenged all of my medical bills that it would one day lead to the formation of my first company, The Karis Group, which would lead in 2014 to a second company, Sedera, and now in 2021 this book. I was 46 when I injured my knee. Now I am 70! Twenty-five years of precious experience with a system that has somehow gone tragically wrong, but where patients and doctors are taking the initiative to put things right.

Thank you for joining me in this journey filled with colorful characters, interesting insights, and hope that brings change.

INTRODUCTION

THERE IS A REVOLUTION GOING ON IN HEALTHCARE in the United States right now, and this book is your opportunity to join the change agents in the process of bringing back sanity to the medical ecosystem. In every other area of national life, American consumers have shown their ability to understand and ultimately make the choices that bring down prices and raise quality. Throughout this book, you will not only learn what others are doing to improve the healthcare system, but also what you can do to be a part of this transformational process.

An ancient Chinese proverb says, "A journey of a thousand miles begins with a single step." Every journey starts somewhere. In a sense, mine began when I finished my medical training and joined a medical practice in a very poor part of London. The East Enders, as the friendly people of this part of town are known, were amazing, but the East End itself was broken. At the time, 92 percent of the population of London's East End lived in government-subsidized housing. When my wife and I moved into the area to join a medical practice, the only home we could find (or afford) was under a slum clearance order, due to be torn down as soon as the local council could demolish it. Seventy years of welfare had turned the whole area into a slum. For one year while we resided there, not one high school sent a single pupil on to any form of higher education—university, teaching training school, or any kind of advanced technical training. All of this made me begin to think about the impacts of systemic poverty, government attempts to help people out of poverty through welfare, and why repeated attempts at providing people with a better life did not seem to work. Until you understand the problem, it is hard to conceive of any answers.

It is no different as we look at where the healthcare system is heading in the United States. What we see here is roughly what Charles Dickens described in the first sentence of his classic, *The Tale of Two Cities*: "It was the best of times; it was the worst of times." People travel from all over the world to the United States for healthcare because they know that they can find the best doctors, hospitals, and medical care that money can buy. But, along with the many centers of excellence that abound, we have a crushing weight of medical debt and despair that is pushing the country to the brink of bankruptcy.

This book is going to help us understand how we got here and what is happening that shows the potential of changing all this for the better. Describing the problem is a useful first step in understanding any problem. But we are all looking for the necessary steps to find a solution, to exchange what is for what can be. That is the goal of this book. Many of the people described in this book have taken steps on their own personal journey to be the change that we need to see in healthcare in this nation.

For most businesses, providing for employee medical care is the highest cost outside of salaries. For most families, healthcare is on par with, or maybe even a higher cost than, their housing or mortgage payments. Is there a way to change this for the average business and for the average family? The answer that is emerging is a resounding yes.

Thank you for taking the time to read this book. But please don't stop with just reading. Get involved. Why be passive when we can be agents of change? Discover where the money is going for your own healthcare and then join the millions who say they will not wait for government or business to come up with the solution. We can take charge of our health, our healthcare, and our healthcare outcomes. So, let's understand what these basic terms mean.

Health describes a condition of wellness, of not being sick. But most healthcare is actually "sickness care." I'm reminded of the Biblical story of a woman with persistent bleeding. Jesus said she spent everything she had and was not getting any better. That clearly is a "sickness system" and sounds remarkably like the situation that so many find themselves in today.

We are going to explore what is happening to bring true **healthcare** to patients across the country. Innovative new approaches to family practice in the form of Direct Primary Care (DPC) and Virtual Primary Care (VPC) are transforming the medical experience for people all over the country as they learn what was taken for granted by their parents' or grandparents' generation, namely the value of the doctor–patient relationship. Relationship implies knowing each other. And as we explore what is happening in this rapidly multiplying movement, we will see a vital first step in moving back to true healthcare with an emphasis on both health and care.

But what happens when we get sick? We often do need a physician to help bring us back to health. This is where healthcare has become so cripplingly expensive. Most doctors did not go into medicine with the thought of getting rich on the backs of patients going through suffering and financial distress. And growing numbers of doctors, some of whom we will meet in the pages of this book, are showing the way to bring medical costs down while bringing medical quality and outcomes up.

By removing middlemen and restoring the direct financial relationship between the doctor and the patient, everybody (except the middleman) wins.

As we will explore later in the book, transparent pricing on its own does not mean that the average sick person will be able to handle the costs of their sickness. We need ways to plan for handling the large medical bills that are likely at some point to impact all of us. How do we plan for this? The presumption has been that we have to have medical insurance. In fact, under the Orwellian named Affordable Care Act (ACA), under which healthcare costs for many people have become even more unaffordable, we are even fined in some states if we don't have medical insurance. But medical insurance—nobody could even pretend that it is "health insurance"—has long since stopped being insurance in any classic sense of that word. Insurance usually means sharing the risk of something expensive that we do not expect to happen, but something we want to be able to take care of if it does happen. Instead, medical insurance has become a very expensive way of pre-paying for things we know are going to happen. And it is precisely here that we see how the new sharing economy provides answers that demonstrate medical insurance is not the best, and clearly not the only, way to handle large medical bills. Millions are finding that for about half the price of medical insurance they can receive better care, find easier access to physicians, and handle large bills through the power of individual choice within a sharing community rather than through government coercion. These are the healthcare outcomes we are looking for.

Whether as individuals or companies, we can choose how we spend our healthcare dollars. After all, if this is the largest expenditure outside of salaries or housing that most of us face, why wouldn't we make smart consumer choices? I chose to challenge the system when I hurt my knee. Join me in challenging the system as you read about the steps that so many people are taking and see how you can be a part of the answer as well.

I'll start by telling part of my story.

CHAPTER 1

IS SOCIALIZED MEDICINE THE ANSWER?

I **AM A FAMILY DOCTOR FROM A LINE** of family doctors. Born in Taiwan, some of my earliest and fondest memories are of going out with my Dad on evening house calls. From the home of the British ambassador, who lived in the old fort that served as the British Embassy in Taiwan, to the ordinary homes of missionaries and businesspeople, to the simple open-air clinics that my father ran for the very poor, I saw every patient treated with loving respect and genuine care. It did not matter whether they paid in cash or with a chicken or, in the case of the really poor, with almost nothing at all. All were welcomed, and all were given the best care that he knew how to give. The love and respect that was accorded to this wonderful, old-fashioned doctor was more than enough to stir in me the desire to follow in his footsteps, even as he had followed in his father's footsteps.

MY EARLY YEARS WORKING IN
THE BRITISH NATIONAL HEALTH SERVICE

Every patient is first of all a person, a unique person to be known and loved and cared for. So often in medical school I had been embarrassed by the grand rounds where 10 or so of us would stand around the patient and the eminent consultant would discuss their "case" as if the patient wasn't even there. Patients are not "a case of this or that." Some of the consultants had a wonderful bedside manner and clearly knew and loved their patients. But most seemed more absorbed in teaching the medical students than caring for the patient. Thankfully, through my father's incredible example, I had learned the foundational nature of the doctor–patient relationship that is so central to real patient care.

But the realities of modern medical practice that I experienced after concluding my medical training in 1975 proved to be something entirely different. Socialized medicine in a very poor part of London was a real eye opener. (Think *Call the Midwife*, for any of you who love medical shows on PBS or Netflix. This remarkable look at the life of a community of midwives, working in the streets right next to where I had my medical practice, will give you some idea of the conditions where we worked.) Seeing 50 patients a day was normal. In flu season, you could double that. As a doctor, I had an average of six minutes with a patient. Add in all of the house calls, the paperwork, and the calls to the local council for help with a patient's social conditions, and there was little time or energy left for friends and family, let alone keeping up to date with medical journals.

Living in this wonderful part of London, the borough of Tower Hamlets, had an equally fascinating impact on my views of economics. I was exposed every day to the impact of "compassionate" socialism over an extended period of time. The National Health Service (NHS), the single-payer system for which Britain is famous, was the only medical option available to 99 percent of the nation's people. Tower Hamlets had had nothing but left-of-center representation for 70 years at this point (except for two years in the 1920s, when it was represented in Parliament by two communists). More than 90 percent of the local residents in our area lived in government-subsidized housing. Who on earth came up with the brilliant idea that you could put so many people with intractable social, health, and mental health problems in the same massive apartment complexes dominating this area of London and expect utopia to appear? The Soviet-style complexes that permeated Tower Hamlets in the 1960s and '70s became slums on the very day they opened and remained that way until they were torn down decades later.

I hate the way that entitlement mentality can trap many people in poverty. I've seen perfectly capable people who—when told that they can't do anything about their unfortunate situations and need the government to do it all for them—are robbed of their desire to improve.

The practice of medicine was fascinating. But quickly I found that I was actually more interested in people than in their medical conditions. You do see the occasional interesting condition, but it is really the people who are so unique. Don't get me wrong; I wanted to be a knowledgeable and effective doctor, but I was rapidly coming to the conclusion that our patients' social conditions were having as much of an impact on their health as the pathology that I studied while a student at the Royal and Ancient Hospital of St. Bartholomew,[1] affectionately known as Barts to all who know London.

East Enders are some of the most unique people in Britain. John and Peta were the first couple we got to know well. John was a builder, and Peta was a teacher at a local elementary school. They brought over a meal to welcome the new couple with a brand new baby to their street and, so they told us, because they liked the bumper stickers on our car! We spent much time in their home, learning about the neighborhood.

One day, while I was doing the dishes after a meal at their house, Peta asked Felicity what we did for work. Felicity mentioned that we both were doctors but that she had left her medical practice when Jonathan, our oldest, was born. On hearing that we were doctors, they were shocked. "You shouldn't be washing the dishes; we can't have doctors doing that!" It was months before they would treat us as "normal" people. British ideas of class were deeply ingrained in the East End.

Many patients come to mind from that era, but one of the most memorable was Mr. Smith. (I have changed his name, as I will with all of my patients. I doubt anyone could find him 45 years after this incident, since he was around 70 when I had my time with him, and I was only 25.) We were in the middle of the junior doctors' strike of 1975,[2] and I was in my medical rotation at one of the hospitals in London's East End. Technically, during the strike, we were only working 40 hours a week except for emergencies. But it was October/November, and the flu was hitting with a vengeance. Everything was an emergency, and when on duty you could pretty much guarantee that you would be working at least an 18-hour day, often more. On the night that Mr. Smith arrived at the hospital, I was the admitting doctor.

Another case of the flu was hardly a surprise, though one had to be really careful—the flu is a serious killer in elderly patients. Death from the flu seemed to be a daily occurrence with this influenza epidemic. I hardly had any time with Mr. Smith, but he needed great nursing care more than time with me. That is, until the morning of his discharge three days later. Hurrying to fit in his discharge medical on a Saturday morning, I could not have imagined what was about to happen.

He was ready to get dressed and head home with his family. Because I couldn't hear his lungs well with him still lying on the bed, I asked him to stand up and turn around so that I could check all was clear by listening to his lungs through his back. As he stood up, he suddenly collapsed.

A quick examination on the floor convinced me he had probably had a cardiac arrest. The crash call went out, and the resuscitation team rushed to the ward where we fought for his life and were able to revive him. The next two weeks were a blur as he hung between life and death in the ICU. Finally, he began to recover and was moved back to the general ward, where I was able to spend more time with him.

Before his cardiac arrest, while keeping an eye on Mr. Smith, I found out that he had four children. Now that he was back on the ordinary ward from the ICU, I was able to take more time with him. I'm so glad that I asked about his children because his oldest child, then in his early 50s, was the chairman of the Area Health Authority in the region where I worked. Within the NHS, this meant that, about 10 layers removed from me, his son was my boss. That is a good thing to know about one of your patients!

Mr. Smith was interesting for other reasons. He had been a cobbler all his life. He made shoes and handbags, but not just any old shoes and handbags. He made shoes and handbags for the Queen—and that is pretty special in England. Now, after almost three weeks in the hospital, he was again ready for discharge. I was called by the ward nurse to come see him before his discharge. To my surprise, as I arrived at his bedside, his first words to me were, "Doctor, I have a present for you. Actually, it's not for you, but for your wife, since I know that I am not allowed to give you anything."

"Why not?" I thought. "It's been hard work keeping you alive!" Then more normal and appreciative thoughts came to mind. As I began to thank him, he told me what was in the package that he had prepared for my wife. It was a handbag that he had made, and it was identical to one he had made for the Queen. I was astounded and rather chagrined at what had passed through my mind. He was so generous with his praise for how I had looked after him that I was honestly rather embarrassed. But it is what happened next that will help you understand why I tell this story.

Faith is an important part of what shapes my thinking. My sense of caring for my patients or trying to help transform the way medical care is paid for in this country grows out of my sense of vocation, of calling. As I walked away from Mr. Smith's bed that morning, with the hand-bag that my wife still treasures, I felt like I could hear God's still, small voice inside me, and I was shocked at what I was hearing, or rather the way it was being said. Is God ever sarcastic?

"Tony, Mr. Smith thinks you're great. In fact, all of the staff here think you are great. There is only one problem. No one knows why."

I immediately knew what God was whispering into my heart. In what little time I had to pray or meditate on what the Bible had to say to me in my busy days during the flu epidemic, I had been meditating on Isaiah 42:8: "I am the Lord; that is my name! I will not give my glory to anyone else, nor share my praise with carved idols."[3] I may have been Mr. Nice Guy and a good doctor and all of that, but if I did not openly acknowledge why that was, how God was at work in my life, then all the glory would go to me and none would go to the true source of all the good in my life. I found myself thinking of another verse that I had learned when I was younger: "God opposes the proud, but gives grace to the humble."[4]

That incident has stayed with me all of these years. If you ask staff members at any of my companies, they will tell you that I honestly believe humility is at the heart, the very foundation, of anything sub-stantial that we can accomplish in our lives. Humility not only makes room for God, but it makes room for others and makes us a conduit for the good things that each of us are called to.[5]

People fascinate me. My faith grounds me and gives me purpose. And systems also fascinate me. I guess you could call this the "big picture syndrome." For example, when I was first invited to become a full partner in a primary care medical practice, I chose to spend some time with the other partners in their clinical (office) context. The first thing to come to my attention was that the patients were waiting forever, or so it seemed to me, to see the doctors. When I asked the office staff, they assured me that patients waiting an hour to see the doctor was the norm and that sometimes, when things were really busy or one of the doctors was out on an urgent house call, waiting times could easily climb to an hour and a half or more.

I really liked the look of the practice, and the partners had very similar ethical views of life to me. I accepted their offer to join, but I had one condition. I felt that respect for the patient demanded that we view their time as important as our own. Would the partners allow me to study patient flow through the practice during my first three months of working with them, and then let me introduce the appointment system of my choice? At first, they were skeptical, presuming that I would abandon my newfangled ideas once I understood more about how people thought and operated within a very poor part of London.

But three months to the day, I called the other doctors together to outline my plan to bring in all patients, except for emergency cases, on the day the patient requested and with a goal of a wait time under 10 minutes. We took a month to regularly communicate what we were planning with our patient population. Then, overnight, we instituted the plans. With approximately one week's worth of gentle chaos, thankfully having planned plenty of extra appointment spaces for all who had not yet heard of the changes, we found that things were working smoothly. To everyone's amazement, including mine, the average wait time had actually dropped overnight to less than five minutes.

SOCIALIZED MEDICINE IS NOT A PANACEA

America is the land of the immigrant. The American dream still draws people from all over the world to this great country and the freedom of opportunity that it represents. Maybe it is the very fact that immigrants have experience with other ways of doing things that gives us insights as this country tries to figure out the best way forward for healthcare. Part of the genius of the great American experiment of 50 states but one nation is the very notion that as different paths are explored, we are able to learn from both the good and the bad of those paths. But we might also learn from the lessons drawn from other nations that have already gone down these roads. A single-payer system can work well in some contexts. But please don't ignore where it is not working very well. Different nations have differing backgrounds, cultures, and core values. Free enterprise is deeply ingrained in the American mythology, the American story. This does not make it automatically correct, but it does mean we ignore it at our peril. I come from a similar nation.

I occasionally blog under the tagline of *Old World Doctor, New World Healthcare*.[6] I am the first to admit that I don't have all of the answers. But I may have some of them, and I have met many people who I believe offer more. As we meet various people in the pages of this book, let's listen to their stories and see if their collective wisdom points to a way forward to lower medical costs, improved quality of care, and dramatically increased access for all.

Dr. Lee Kurisko's experience closely parallels my own. He was a Canadian family doctor who became Board-certified in radiology. He was rapidly climbing in the Canadian national health system, a system very similar to the structure of the NHS. Passionate about medical care, patients, and his native country's commitment to healthcare free for all at the point of service, he found his youthful idealism being rapidly eroded. What happened? Let him tell his story in his own words:

Each day, between doing angiograms, I hurriedly review a stack of 50 or more MRI requisitions. In charge of the only MRI for 250,000 people and a geographical area the size of France, I must triage the relentless onslaught of requisitions in an attempt to prioritize the most urgent cases to the front of the queue. Due to funding limitations, only about 20 cases can be done daily. But the waiting list grows relentlessly, with no end in sight. With a sick feeling in my stomach, I review the day's requests . . .

As the months passed, my anxiety over the ever-growing length of our MRI waiting list nearly overwhelmed me. I was sickened by the notion that any of them could have unrecognized but treatable illnesses . . .

No longer in a trainee role and carrying the responsibility of trying to make the system work, my naivety rapidly vanished. In less than two years, I became the medical director of Diagnostic Imaging at Thunder Bay Regional Hospital. This rapid ascent largely reflects the fact that there was simply no one else to do it . . . As a medical director, I soon came to see the impoverishment rendered by the government-controlled system of Canadian healthcare. Along with material resources such as X-ray machines, the system is impoverished for competent people . . .

Canadian state-run healthcare disallows the ownership and operation of private surgical clinics and private MRI and CAT scan centers. Government policy disallows citizens from obtaining services at such facilities. In Canada, doctors are forced to work for the state and accept it as their paymaster. Taxpayers are forced to pay for the system, and patients are forced to receive their care from this system . . .

Canadian universal healthcare is incompatible with the notion of rights . . .

It is astounding that, in light of the Canadian experience, people in the United States think Americans should embrace the Canadian style of healthcare . . .

I detested being forced into the role of a bureaucrat who played God with people's lives.[7]

Everything that Dr. Kurisko describes here is virtually identical to what has been described to us as Medicare for All. It is literally for all. No one is allowed to purchase private health insurance under this policy.[8] Doctors are not free to practice medicine as they wish. No one may opt out; this essentially ends private practice. There is no doubt that different people are using the term "Medicare For All" in different ways. So far, Medicare for All has not become the official policy of either political party, but it is clearly the direction that the Affordable Care Act, and subsequent leadership in some circles, wants to take us. Whether this leadership, given the chance, would actually outlaw private practice is unknown.

In light of this ongoing discussion within American political circles, it is hardly surprising that Dr. Kurisko, a Canadian physician, or I, as a former active and willing participant in the NHS, would now want to help people understand that the socialized approach to medicine is not the panacea that many naively proclaim it to be. Waiting lists are the norm in both the UK and Canada.

Are there good things about the British and Canadian systems? Definitely. But identifying the benefits of these systems is not the same as saying they would be good for the United States. The stories you will read in this book, and the ideas that we will explore, will outline why America doesn't need a single-payer system. America is on the way to a renewal of compassionate capitalism and free enterprise through the remarkable resurgence already happening in free market medical care across the United States.

American healthcare is in crisis. Everyone agrees there is much wrong with the healthcare system. Can it be transformed? Will this transformation come through reformation or through revolution? As philosopher Ivan Illich put it when asked this question in a different context, the answer may be neither reformation nor revolution. Instead, we must learn to tell a different story.

Dr. Kurisko loves to tell that different story. Here are the key points that he is bringing to our attention:

It behooves us all to heed Thomas Jefferson's dire warning: "Government big enough to supply everything that you need is big enough to take everything that you have . . . The course of history shows that as government grows, liberty decreases." In my former life as Medical Director of Diagnostic Imaging of Thunder Bay Regional Hospital, I had a waiting list of 13 months for MRIs and seven months for CAT scans. The angiography equipment was old and decrepit, and I lost many hours of sleep as I worried about delivering care under these conditions.[9]

The Founding Fathers' brilliance goes unseen by most people. They realized that society works best when as much decision-making as possible occurs at the individual level. That is why the Founding Fathers preferred a limited, small, and non-intrusive government. As Jefferson noted, "The government that governs least, governs best.[10]

If one argues that government should assume the decision-making power for our healthcare, there is no logical reason why government should not assume decision-making power for any aspect of our lives. The logical extension of government-run healthcare is the personal abrogation of individual rights and subjugation, without rights, to the laws of the State.[11]

Dr. Kurisko and I are both first-generation immigrants. We have both worked as physicians under a socialized system. I never carried the authority that he did within the system. But both of us have come to a similar conclusion. Let's build on what is good within the American system. Yes, there is much that is bad. But let's build on natural American strengths. As we read on, we are going to learn more about the great things that are already happening within the system by transformation from the bottom up rather than changes forced from the top down.

In 2019, I was admitted via the ER for the extraction of a kidney stone trapped in the ureter. My hospital bill was close to $30,000, which was "generously" discounted to $15,000 with a cash-pay discount. My question is: Which price is accurate, or are they both a lie? Isn't a 50-percent discount for cash payment still a form of extortion when the "rack rate" of $30,000 has no relationship to the real cost? If the hospital had been happy to deal with me as a Medicare patient, the government would have paid $3,000 for the same service. What makes it a "great price" when the cash payment is five times as high and is presented to the cash payer as a great favor? This isn't a game; it's a form of theft!

In this book, I try to explore my own entrepreneurial journey, and that of many other fellow travelers on this path who are already transforming American healthcare.

CHAPTER 2

THE PRICE WE PAY

I HAD JUST ARRIVED AT THE COLONOSCOPY UNIT for my routine colonoscopy. Knowing the system, I had pre-arranged a cash price that was
50 percent off the standard price for this group of gastroenterologists.
Having completed the grueling preparation of the day before, I arrived
hungry, grouchy, and ready to have this procedure behind me.

The helpful receptionist welcomed me on arrival, but immediately
let me know that the practice was not going to be able to perform the
procedure. Apparently, the price that I had pre-negotiated could not be
honored without breaking their Medicare contract. This contract required
that they never accept a lower price than their Medicare-contracted price.

"Would you like to pay the full price and move forward with the
colonoscopy today?" she asked.

Shocked, I asked in return if they were seriously asking a patient who
was fully prepped for a colonoscopy if they wanted to either pay double

the price or have to reschedule. When she told me that those were my only possible choices, I asked if their center really wanted to turn away a doctor who had gone through this prep and was also letting them know that their information was incorrect. Medicare does not forbid doctors from accepting a cash payment below the Medicare rate.

Maybe because I was a doctor, the receptionist went for help. Twenty minutes later, she returned and told me that my concerns had been pushed all the way up the chain of command to the CEO of this august practice of about 30 gastroenterologists. The CEO was not only an MD but also an attorney. The receptionist told me that the practice would now honor the agreed-upon price. However, so as not to contravene their Medicare contract, they had notified the doctor performing the procedure that he would have to pay the remaining 50 percent out of his own pocket to bring my procedure up to the practice list price!

Everything about this story is completely wrong. The practice's approach was both absolutely immoral and against the most basic understanding of medical ethics and practice. To start with, even if the practice had been correct in their understanding of their own Medicare contract, they should have apologized to me for their misunderstanding and offered to move forward with the procedure at no additional charge. It is totally wrong to refuse to serve a patient who is already fully prepped for a surgical procedure of this type. Secondly, the idea that they told the doctor who was about to perform a potentially life-threatening procedure that it was going to cost him $1,200 to do the work hardly gave me the confidence that he would have my best interests at heart. The surgeon even mentioned before the procedure that the CEO had told him he would be paying for my colonoscopy out of his own pocket. This was definitely not reassuring to me as the patient. Thankfully, the surgeon himself had good medical ethics, and all went well.

After getting home, I wrote to the CEO and pointed out that I thought his legal opinion regarding the Medicare contract was in error. About a month later, I received a response acknowledging that they were wrong and I was right. But the letter offered no other apology for the way I was treated. When I wrote back and asked if the CEO would like to have lunch with me to discuss why the cash-pay patient was their best possible patient, the invitation never led to anything. Maybe I shouldn't have expected it to. But I grew up in a world where doctors were always courteous and friendly to other doctors.

What has gone wrong in a system where things like this happen? As the famous line from the movie, *All the President's Men*, goes, "Follow the money." Deep Throat never spoke truer words. Dr. Daneshgari, a world-famous urologist and university professor who I will say more about in a later chapter, has this to say about pricing transparency: "One of the events that pushed me toward stepping down from my chair position was when I saw a bill for a vasectomy I had done on a patient at the Medical Center for $9,000. My patient's out of pocket/deductible was $1,000!"

Vasectomies can easily be done in the doctor's office for around $250 or at a Planned Parenthood facility for around $200. No wonder hospitals can afford endless billboards and airport advertising to persuade patients that they are the best around. The financial harm done to our patients by this exorbitant billing is a breach of our oath to "first do no harm."

I was talking with a close friend about their experience as a surgical resident in Texas. One of the resident's colleagues had recently done a minor surgical procedure in the ER that had taken about 10 minutes. For this brief treatment, the patient was billed $16,000! The resident was shocked. We have to find a way to take a stand against such excesses within the medical system.

If these were isolated incidents, they might possibly be excused as careless pricing. But that is not the case, as Dr. Marty Makary has extensively documented in his book, *The Price We Pay*.[1] He tells one story about a hospital in New Mexico that has even sued its own staff for not paying their exorbitant hospital bills. Apparently, this hospital has literally sued thousands of people in the town they serve. The perverse nature of the *system* now includes such absurdities as nonprofit hospitals actually suing their patients for unpaid medical bills that are ridiculously high in the first place. Dr. Makary's writing makes compelling reading. But what adds even greater authenticity to this is the fact that he often helps patients who reach out to him by testifying on their behalf in court cases where the patient is being sued by the hospital. This level of personal involvement is gripping. It is involvement that will ultimately change the system for the better. Dr. Makary challenges all of us to speak up. The current public and political conversation around medical policy issues is essentially dishonest. And those who understand that this is dishonest need to speak out to bring truth into the medical conversation.

The utter lack of pricing transparency, along with the unnecessary complexity with which medical bills are presented, makes it all but impossible even for an expert to understand exactly what he or she is being charged for. When nonprofit hospitals and clinics with religious structures that also benefit from the public's generosity in allowing them not to pay taxes actively pursue these same policies, the practice moves from absurd to perversely evil. It makes me think of what the Apostle Paul wrote 2,000 years ago: "Have nothing to do with the fruitless deeds of darkness, but rather expose them."[2]

THE IMPORTANCE OF THE FREE MARKET

In the emerging free market healthcare economy, the consumer can choose where their healthcare dollars go. We are not powerless. Every time I go to a pharmacy, I can pull out my GoodRx card and ask if my prescription costs less if I use this simple mechanism. When my doctor tells me that I need an X-ray or lab work, I can take a little time to find out what this procedure will cost me as a cash payer. As a company CEO, I can demand that I see value for my employees in whatever approach I take in helping with their healthcare costs. It is inexcusable for me to delegate the second largest expense in my company's P&L (Profit and Loss) to a benefits expert (the broker) who is paid by insurance companies and may not even know that there are non-insurance solutions for handling company medical costs. There is also no reason for the government to force a business to use an insurance model to handle employee healthcare, when non-insurance models are emerging that do a better job with greater transparency.

In our current medical economic model, ignorance is not bliss. We are all paying the price of ever-increasing health insurance costs and the loss of income this represents. We must take personal responsibility for understanding what is happening, then take action. As a company founder, I can make sure that we use the purchasing power of the healthcare we provide to our staff to help drive the movement towards transparent pricing. As an individual, I can make sure I take the personal responsibility to find out how I can get fair pricing rather than just letting the system overcharge me. The nature of the corporate medical-industrial system may be perverse, but that is no excuse for just putting up with it. We have personal accountability for the money we spend and for the money we allow to be spent on our behalf. If we don't like the thinking that has allowed the system to become this corrupt, then we must do the hard work that will lead to the changes the system needs.

In this context of systemic corruption, the most amazing people are finding ways to change things from the bottom up. As we explore their stories, we must not only admire what they have done but also find ways to join them in these tasks. For the system to change, each of us must find ways to spend our healthcare dollars with providers who honor fair payments. They are not always easy to find. But if we don't support the brave medical providers who are driving medical transparency based on honest pricing, how can these providers survive when the whole system is stacked against them?

In my experience, change in a good direction does not usually happen without some hard work. And this work begins within our minds. Let's explore how our thinking shapes our outcomes.

CHAPTER 3

HOW WE THINK MATTERS

S TEPHEN COVEY, IN HIS BEST-SELLING BOOK, *The Seven Habits of Highly Successful People*, coined the phrase, "Begin with the end in mind." This is the second of his seven "habits," and it is a great place for us to begin to understand what must change in the healthcare system.

Most of us have heard of Albert Einstein's famous maxim, "The thinking that got us to where we are is not the thinking that will get us to where we want to be." The answer to healthcare's challenges is not some type of incremental change to the system as it currently exists. Rather, we need to learn to think differently. For the past 75 or more years, the American healthcare system has been dominated by the thinking that improving health insurance will somehow improve healthcare. But healthcare and health insurance are two totally different things.

The Affordable Care Act exemplified this thinking when mandating health insurance under penalty of law, presuming that "coverage" equals "access." But it does not. Many people are covered under Medicaid or Medicare, but it does not mean that they have easy access to healthcare. As mentioned, I was trained as a physician under the British socialized system. Everyone was covered, but that was no guarantee that everyone could see a doctor when they needed to see one. The system effectively rationed access to care as a way of controlling costs. In both Britain and Canada, where universal coverage for all citizens is a right, you can easily wait months for an MRI and sometimes years for a hip replacement. We all want to see better healthcare. But whoever said that the only way to get this is through better health insurance?

Doctors and their many colleagues in nursing and other medically related professions provide access to healthcare. No insurance company can ever provide access to that healthcare. Don't get me wrong. The insurance company may be able to provide a path toward payment for healthcare, but history shows that it is an expensive path, littered with the good intentions of politicians and policy makers. It is the doctor, first and foremost, who provides the care.

THE GREEK ROOTS OF HEALTHCARE PHILOSOPHIES

As we look for ways to fix the American healthcare system, we need to be aware that two different and competing philosophies handed down to us from Greek philosophers influence the form and variety of proposed solutions. In the Platonic worldview, exemplified in modern life by the ACA, the State is supreme, not God (or the gods). Via the elite stratum of society, the State makes the decisions for all members of the State. In contrast, in the worldview of the physician and philosopher Hippocrates, the individual is supreme and, as noted in our Declaration of Independence, "endowed by their Creator with certain unalienable rights." These unalienable rights are the foundation of liberty. Personhood is granted by the gods, and the life of every individual is sacred.

At the time the Declaration of Independence was drafted, the thinking of Hippocrates was (fortunately) the dominant sentiment. As masterfully explained in Dr. C.L. Gray's book, *The Battle for America's Soul*, the American Declaration of Independence was built on the foundational understanding that individual people are "endowed by their Creator with certain unalienable rights" precisely because it is clear that we are all subject to "the laws of nature and of nature's God."[1] Our fundamental right to "life, liberty and the pursuit of happiness" is God-given. We need to understand that this philosophy is a fundamental component of our worldview, our basic understanding of the "why" rather than the "what," and that it shapes how we see the world. If our fundamental right to "life, liberty and the pursuit of happiness" were to be given to us by the State, then the State could also take it away. I don't want that. But that is what medical professionals in the United States are faced with in the form of the Affordable Care Act and other government mandates.

Our rights to "life, liberty and the pursuit of happiness" are not granted by the State. Those rights supersede the authority of the State because they are part of what Americans understand as being "self-evident that all men are created equal and have certain unalienable rights." Unalienable means that no one can take away something given freely to all people by God. This is why the Declaration of Independence and the Bill of Rights are so important. My rights are not more important than your rights. Rather, all rights are freely given, and the role of limited government is to protect those rights.

We can explore the healthcare conundrum by looking at the doctor–patient relationship. To do this, it is helpful to go back in time to the ancient Greeks and explore their influence on philosophy and medicine.

Plato, perhaps the most famous of the Greek philosophers and the author of *The Republic*, believed that the ideal society had three classes of people:

1. Producers or Workers: The laborers who supply a society with goods and services

2. Guardians/Soldiers: Those who keep order in a society and defend it from invaders

3. Philosopher Kings: The most intelligent, rational, self-controlled, in love with wisdom, and well suited to make decisions for the community, and who promote the interests of the society as a whole[2]

In Plato's ideal society, the State is supreme, the elites make the decisions, and the common person is a vassal of the State. Essentially, everything belongs to the State. Democracy is a danger because it provides a way for ordinary people, with their base or selfish desires unchecked, to attain ultimate power.

In contrast to this system of thinking, Hippocrates taught and practiced medicine on the basis of the individual being the place of ultimate value. Their personhood came from the gods. The value of even one life was absolute. The Hippocratic Oath stated plainly that "first you must do no harm." Abortion was specifically forbidden because only the gods could give or withhold life. In the Platonic model, the value of a life was based on the value the State placed on that life. A doctor can, and must, take a life if dictated by the State. The infirm or the slave or the criminal could be appropriately killed by the doctor at the dictates of the State.[3] In contrast, in the Hippocratic tradition, no doctor would consider such a demand from the State.

In case you are wondering whether these ancient and abstract ideas have any serious impact on healthcare, consider the following as quoted from the *Wall Street Journal* article published by Betsy McCaughey on

August 27, 2009. The issue being addressed is concern for the individual patient versus concern for the impact of medical decisions on society as a whole.

> Dr. Emanuel believes doctors should serve two masters, the patient and society, and that medical students should be trained "to provide socially sustainable, cost-effective care." . . . "[T]he progression in end-of-life care mentality from 'do everything' to more palliative care shows that change in physician norms and practices is possible."[4]

The understanding of the "value" of life is explicitly explained in Dr. Emanuel's famous graph known generally as the "reaper curve." In this graph, it is clear that as an individual's contribution to society goes down, the dollar value of scarce healthcare resources equally goes down. It is a short step from this thinking to euthanasia and infanticide.

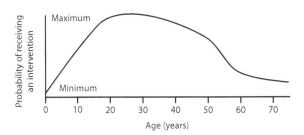

The Reaper Curve: Ezekiel Emanuel used the above chart in a *Lancet* article to illustrate the ages on which health spending should be focused.

"Principles for allocation of scarce medical interventions." *The Lancet*, January 31, 2009

Why we do things ends up shaping how and what we do. Whether we understand this or not, it still shapes our actions. Everybody has a worldview, a "why," whether or not we acknowledge or even understand it.

The competing philosophies of Plato (who gives all power to and centralizes the importance of the State) and Hippocrates (who does the same for the individual) are at the heart of the political battles for control of American healthcare. The different philosophies lead to different conclusions for how to manage the economics of healthcare. The Platonic worldview dictates that elites make decisions for all of us, ostensibly to bring the greatest benefit to society as a whole. The Hippocratic worldview dictates that the individual makes the decision that is best for them and that focusing on the greatest benefit to individuals will create the greatest benefits to society as a whole.

How you think matters.

THE WRONG INCENTIVES

When I worked as a family doctor with the NHS, I had little understanding of the implications of these philosophical ideas but, gradually, the workings of the system made it plain. My time was not valued by many of my patients because I was available for free. But the same attitudes began to infect my naïve presumptions about my own good intentions. Because it made little if any difference to how I was treated or paid, there was always the tendency to cut corners. I like to think of myself as a doctor who would always go the extra mile. But external motivations can certainly help.

Why have we been taught that the only motivation needed in healthcare is the generous heart of the provider, when we all intuitively know that we get the best service not from the generous heart of the bureaucrat but from the engaged concern of the well-paid employee? What makes us imagine doctors as such saints? A bad bedside manner or incompetence in medical care should lead to a doctor's patients feeling free to find another medical provider. Similarly, loving concern for the patient, as exemplified in great doctor–patient relationships, should lead to as much work as the doctor chooses to have and at a price that is perceived as a win-win by both doctor and patient.

Yet, the system militates against this, often robbing doctors of their independence without them even realizing this. More and more medical practices are being bought out by the hospitals around them. The siren call is the convenience of your practice being managed by someone else, leaving you free to really focus on your patients. But the real reason is so the local hospital can "control" the doctor through a variety of financial incentives. You will get paid extra for how many patients you refer to the specialty and other facilities (such as labs and X-rays) owned by that hospital.

Now, instead of telling your patient about the $350 MRI just down the road from the hospital, you are incentivized to send the patient to the hospital MRI unit, where it will cost the patient thousands out of their deductible for the same procedure. If you don't refer enough patients into the hospital care system, then don't expect any bonus. It is no longer up to you to help out the poorer patient by waiving their fees if you wish. Instead, you may find the owners of your practice suing the patient for not paying the full charge, over which you now have no control.

The contrast between what is described here and what is experienced when the free market is set loose is staggering. To understand this, let's compare how we deal with other decisions that have a significant financial impact on us.

If I want to buy a big screen TV, there is a bewildering array of options. Nobody is forced to buy a big screen TV, yet virtually everybody chooses to do so. Why is this? Ten years ago, if you wanted a 60-inch television, it might have cost you $8,000. Hardly anybody had one that large. Hardly anyone could afford it. Every person made their own choices, and most could live with a much smaller television set. Each of us weighed for ourselves the value we placed on a larger or smaller television, and a few of us just went without a television altogether. What I am describing is the free market. Market forces left to themselves without outside interference from government or other price-fixing schemes, such as monopolies and cartels, interact with the consumer based on what is known as the law of supply and demand. And supply and demand rapidly bring the price down, whether you are talking about a big screen TV or Lasik surgery.

We all know that if there is more of something, the price comes down. If last summer was perfect weather for the growth of vegetables, then the price of vegetables went down in the supermarkets. If this summer has been too wet for healthy growth, and what little that did grow rotted in the fields in very wet conditions, then the price will go up. This is the *supply* side of the economic equation. But we need to also look at the *demand* side. Let's take the electric car industry. When Tesla came out with its first model at around $100,000, lots of us would have been happy to buy one if we could afford it. But until they began talking about a car in the more normal $30–50,000 range, it was unlikely that most of us would seriously consider buying it. My wanting to *buy* something is the demand side of the equation.

Now consider what happens when, rather than just letting normal market forces set prices, we allow outside interference. Maybe lobbyists find a way to persuade politicians that all health insurance must cover birth control. This is an affront to *some* peoples' religious beliefs, and it increases the cost of insurance for everyone. Why not have available insurance that pays for birth control and insurance that does not pay for birth control? The same could be said of virtually every other mandate that is added to an insurance plan.

Maybe I prefer to make healthy lifestyle choices and pay for a skinny health insurance plan rather than spending my money on covering everything that is inevitable if I constantly make poor lifestyle choices. Health insurance is a way to pool risk. But why should I have to pay the premium, by force of law, for others who choose to smoke or drink dangerous amounts of alcohol or use illegal drugs? If we allow the free market to guide the price of health insurance, then surely it will help people with unhealthy lifestyles think more carefully about the choices that they make. Disincentives in the form of more money out of one's pocket can be powerful motivators.

Think about this in relation to what you see currently in American healthcare. We have a product, health insurance, that everyone has to buy. Competition has been massively curtailed by government mandates and interference so that only a few companies have survived in any given market and almost all innovation is stifled. It is almost impossible for new entrants to move into this field. Forcing demand, even when people don't feel that they are getting value for money, means that costs go up rather than down. Protecting giant insurance companies and their profit margins means that, if they want to create larger profits, it is not greater quality or more efficiency that they need but larger premiums!

HEALTHCARE IS NOT A RIGHT

Similar philosophic issues come into play when we start thinking about whether healthcare is a "right." Let's look at this question because where we start from in our thinking dictates where we are likely to end up.

The fundamental question is this: Where do our "rights" come from? When the Declaration of Independence says that we have "certain unalienable rights," these are not something the State gives to us at the expense of other people but something that God gives to us without charge. Everybody has the right to live, but that right does not infringe on anyone else's rights or cost anyone else anything. There is no right to "happiness" but just to the "pursuit of happiness." These rights are unalienable precisely because they are seen and experienced in the "laws of nature and of nature's God." This is the "life, liberty and the pursuit of happiness" that makes so many around the world long to come to America. They are looking for the freedom to pursue these things.

The power to tax is enormously important when we consider ways to improve our healthcare system. We know that "Medicare for All" begins by both repealing Medicare as we currently know it and also by outlawing private medical care.[5] Ask the Canadians how that is working out for them, with their waiting lists and outdated or nonexistent medical equipment in many regions. It is hardly surprising that so many of their citizens choose to come south to get urgently needed medical care here.

This is the key difference between Plato and Hippocrates or between a socialist/communist state and a democracy based on unalienable rights. The British form of government, known as a constitutional monarchy, evolved over time from a statist concept that God had given ownership of everything to the King (known as "the divine right of kings") to a model that recognized that the King (the State) had no divine right, only God-given responsibility to protect the true rights and ownership privileges of the people. If the State is king, then the State can take ownership by force. This usually is known in socialist societies as nationalizing something, and this is a form of State-sponsored theft. When Canada decided that all healthcare must be provided by the government, Canada was denying the rights of those in the medical profession to ply their trade freely. Why can a baker choose how he wants to run his business, but a doctor may not?

Understanding these issues is at the root of the differences of opinion between doctors who put the patient, the individual, first and those who choose to put the apparent good of the group, of society, first.

Doctors like Ezekiel Emanuel, whose philosophy as health advisor to President Barack Obama helped shape the ACA, believe that it is vital to work for the greater good of society rather than focusing on a patient's needs.[6] This leads to rationing care on the basis of age or usefulness to society. As a physician myself, and I know many other doctors who feel the same way, I find this viewpoint very damaging to my relationship with my patients. I am pledged to do the best that I can for the patient in front of me. This whole principle is brilliantly argued by Dr. Accad of the Accad and Koka Report in his book, *Moving Mountains*.[7]

Dr. Elaina George, whose Atlanta-based ENT practice is mentioned elsewhere in this book, also comments very passionately about this subject. "Taken to its logical extent, [the Affordable Care Act] would have created a world where the 'good of the many,' by definition must outweigh the needs of the few . . . Population health outcomes are what matter, not individual cure or care."

This fundamental difference in understanding of the role of the physician as focused on the patient in front of them rather than focused on the "health of society" leads to very different outcomes in the practice of medical care. On a number of occasions in my own practice, I found myself facing a young couple who came to see me when it was evident that the man wanted his girlfriend to "get rid of the baby." But so often the woman was already strongly attached to the child within her and was expressing her desire for the new life to be allowed to thrive. However, the boyfriend and often her family were saying, "Let's just get rid of it!" Even society in this situation is likely thinking, "The last thing we need is another unwanted child in this poor part of London." But as the doctor of this mother carrying a child in her womb, I was thinking, "This is a life we are talking about, and the mother doesn't want to terminate it. The mother and the baby are my patients and I want to protect them both."

With these ideas buzzing around in my mind, it was natural for me to think, "What can I do about these challenges?" Actions speak louder than words, and actions need to accompany our ideas. My own entrepreneurial journey was the natural consequence.

CHAPTER 4

MY ENTREPRENEURIAL JOURNEY

THE SCREAMING COULD BE HEARD throughout the whole concourse. We weren't the only ones looking alarmed. People everywhere were looking to see the cause of the disturbance. At the center of it all was Becky, my three-year-old daughter, vigorously protesting that she did not want to be fingerprinted! We had just arrived at Houston Intercontinental Airport from England. We were the modern version of "give me your tired, your poor, your huddled masses yearning to breathe free."[1] The six of us, Felicity and I and our four bone-weary kids ranging in age from 3 to 10, were going through immigration, which apparently included all of us being fingerprinted. That is, all of us except the loudly protesting Becky.

The journey from that memorable day in October 1987, when six tired travelers and 12 of the largest boxes the airline would allow finally arrived in Austin, Texas, to where we are now has been remarkable. Our departure from England was delayed by one day due to the first hurricane in modern history hitting the British Isles. (The previous one wrecked the Spanish Armada in 1588.) This one appeared to precipitate "Black Monday," when the Dow Jones Industrial Average dropped 508 points in a single day. Or maybe that was caused by word getting out that the Dales had just landed.

The past 33-plus years for this immigrant family have been one enormous adventure. We've found things here to love and admire, we've been disappointed in a few more, but most importantly we've found things here worth standing up for. We may not have been penniless on arrival, but we got there (penniless, that is) as fast as we could. Within two years, we went from having plenty of cash in the bank (savings from 10 years of medical work) to being virtually broke. And that is where we stayed until good fortune, God's grace, and years of hard work put us on the rollercoaster toward the American dream and the call of God on my life.

Along the way, through the ups and downs of life, we have seen some of the best and the worst of America. I have come to love this country. I think I always did. I remember as a kid in London going to Saturday matinee movies and watching Roy Rogers and the Lone Ranger and Tonto. Any country that big, and where the good guys always catch the bad guys, must be an awesome place to live. I think I have a more realistic and robust view of America now than I did then, but the dream is still as much about vision as reality, hope as contrasted with daily experience. I didn't cross the ocean for more of the daily grind but to fulfill a vision of what was possible. And for that same reason, countless others still risk life and limb, safety and comfort, even close family ties to come to this great land. Whatever is wrong with this place, there is still much more that is right.

My background is that of a British physician who came here, not to practice medicine, but to follow a call. I don't mean just healthcare, though we will focus on that. Let's explore what it is that makes this a healthy or unhealthy place to be.

You have no idea how large your neighborhood supermarket is. I don't mean that you don't know how many square feet of space there is in the store. But you may not understand how huge it seems when you come from another country—even when you come from another affluent country. England is not poor according to the world rankings on poverty, but when we came here in 1987, we were astounded by how big the supermarkets were. I don't even like to shop. But it was an outing to remember as we went to our local H-E-B (equivalent to Randalls or Albertsons or Safeway, or even the food section of a Super Walmart). How do you find marmalade in a place this size? And it wasn't just the size of the stores that was different. When we went food shopping, we received a firsthand education about cultural differences—if they have 10 types of marmalade in our little stores in England, why do these stores in America have only two types and no Marmite?

Never had we seen such abundance. Stores everywhere! In London in 1987, we had only one true "mall" that I am aware of, and that was for a city of 10 million people. We arrived in Austin (population approximately 350,000 in 1987), and there were huge malls everywhere.

We bought our first house here for $135,000, sight unseen. It came with five acres of land. When our kids woke up that first morning in our new home, they thought we had moved to wonderland. Even the Queen couldn't have this much space in the middle of London. We were overwhelmed—and it came at such a low price! Our 1,000-square-foot house in England was on the market for triple that price. Now we were living in a "park," or so it seemed to us, and we had our own pool and hot tub. Surely this was the "promised land," and we had crossed the Red Sea safely.

REALITY SETS IN

It's hard to remember exactly when reality began to set in. I have lived here for 33 years now and, having a naturally positive disposition, I find it easy to forget the hard times. What I do remember is knowing we would run out of money pretty quickly if I couldn't figure out how to earn a living. I may be a doctor, but no one cares how famous your medical school is if you don't have a license to practice medicine in whichever country you are in.

Actually, we didn't come here to practice medicine. When we moved here, I was working for a British Christian medical organization that I had helped start in the late 1970s. Caring Professions Concern, as it was known, had spread rapidly across the UK and various other countries, and I thought we might expand the work here in the United States. But that work quickly dried up. And because I wasn't licensed to practice medicine in the U.S., I had to find something quickly that would help me feed my family.

I didn't expect Amway to be my knight in shining armor. Jared and Astrid Rowe typify the American dream to me. Jared was a retired Army colonel with several tours of duty in Vietnam under his belt. He built his Amway business to the Diamond level in his spare time. Now Jared lived to help other newbies in the business, like me, figure out how we could garner our own slice of the American pie.

Astrid is the perfect partner for business and life. Organized, down to earth, and intelligent, she runs their Amway sales organization meticulously, and she was always available to help any of us who were having difficulty getting our businesses off the ground. German by birth, but American by choice (and by marriage), she typifies what is possible for those who are willing to work hard, learn new skills, and live by Zig Ziglar's creed that if you help enough other people achieve what they want, you will always end up with what you want. Astrid loves helping people get what they want. So, the business grew, or at least it did for us.

Quickly we found ourselves Amway Directs and in short order Ruby Directs. But nothing lasting comes without some "blood, toil, tears and sweat," as Winston Churchill once famously told the British government. To maintain this rapid growth, I built our Amway business mainly around the joint venture between Amway and MCI, the long-distance phone company. For a couple of years, the income from this remarkable marketing partnership was solid, even if the work was hard. I canvassed flea markets, government housing projects, and stores frequented by a Hispanic population making lots of long-distance and international calls and eager to learn ways to save money.

Then, overnight, the FCC changed some of the rules related to marketing MCI, and our business evaporated into thin air. This was not the last time that something we had built through hard work would disappear at the whim of some distant regulator outside of our control. Such are the delights of being an entrepreneur. All the cheering and shouting and feel-good experiences of the Amway conventions couldn't change the fact that we were back where we had started—broke and wondering how we would pay the bills next month.

However, while life (and government regulations) may deal you the occasional challenge, it is how you react to it that makes the greatest impact on who you are and what you become. As Churchill put it in another of his famous speeches, "Never, never, never give up." Without my Amway experiences, and God's gracious work in our hearts, I doubt I would have had the courage and tenacity to plow on, daring to believe I could create something out of nothing. To me, this is the heart of the American opportunity.

GOVERNMENT AND THE POVERTY TRAP

You never get something for nothing in life. It's hard to value what you don't pay for and, in my experience, you come to despise those who give it to you. When you have as many people in a country who don't pay income tax as those who do, it is not only the "have nots" who are suffering, but also the "haves." As Solomon taught us in Proverbs, "It is the hand of the diligent that makes rich."

Having worked as a family doctor in the heart of London's East End for 10 years, I had seen the impact of multigenerational government handouts. Welfare, certainly for the second generation onwards, breeds a dependence that is as addictive as it is destructive. Nearly all of us hit times in life when we need some help. But how that help is offered, for how long, by whom, and with what accompanying responsibility makes a huge difference to its long-term impact. Studies in Michigan from 1992 through 2002 showed that the framework provided by changes in social legislation enabled roughly 308,000 families to move out of the poverty trap and into ongoing employment. By providing a framework that actively encouraged employment, and by modifying welfare benefits such that a dollar earned did not automatically mean losing a dollar or, often more, in benefits, people quickly saw the value of increasing their earnings. Similarly, quoting from a paper[2] written for the Berkeley Symposium on Poverty and Demographics, "In August 1996, the Congress passed and President Clinton signed the Personal Responsibility and Work Opportunity Reconciliation Act (PRWORA). Many pieces of legislation are heralded as "pathbreaking reform" when they are passed. PRWORA was an exception in that such a claim has turned out to be correct."

The nature of taxation is that it is coercive. All who have much can, and many will, freely give of their abundance. I doubt Jesus was joking when he said, "It is more blessed to give than to receive." But the issue here is in the giving. When you are forced to give, there is little blessing in the giving. And when you have a "right" to receive, there is no blessing in the receiving either. It becomes demeaning and actually brings the one receiving into a place of unhealthy dependence. This is the poverty trap.

The promise of America is that if you work, you will not only eat but also eat well. So why rob the poor of the chance to eat well by entrapping them with the handouts of a benevolent government?

If Warren Buffett wants to give more of his money to the government when he dies, then let him. Yet I can't help but notice that he wisely gave the vast majority of it to the Bill and Melinda Gates Foundation. It is much more likely to be effective there than in government hands. That was his choice. I likewise choose to put a certain percentage of my company profits into charitable giving while putting significant amounts of my personal income and time into charitable causes.

When the government wants the top four percent of wage earners in America to pay for the health and upkeep of the bottom 45 percent, they are robbing both the rich and the poor. In a comment usually attributed to Lincoln but probably penned by Rev. Boetcker in a famous tract that he wrote, he said, "You cannot bring about prosperity by discouraging thrift. You cannot strengthen the weak by weakening the strong."

I remember when Hong Kong was a bastion of British sensibility in economics and the thriving hub of international trade in the Far East. It had a flat tax of 15 percent on everyone, rich and poor. At that level, there is little motivation to avoid paying taxes. In fact, most people considered it a privilege, at that time, to live in Hong Kong. Until recent crackdowns, even under the leadership of China's Communist party, Hong Kong actually scored higher on the "economic freedom index" than the United States.

Some fascinating experiments going on around the world help us understand how we can help people out of poverty. The Grameen Bank in Bangladesh comes to mind. Instead of handouts, they have helped millions of people out of poverty by providing microloans. Notice these are loans. Even the poorest of the poor are delighted to repay their loans when treated with dignity and respect. Repayment rates are approximately 98 percent.

If you fail to take note of the fact that most so-called healthcare is actually "sick care," you will inevitably fail to understand why we have an endless spiral of rising costs and diminishing returns. When this vital area of the overall economy also represents nearly 20 percent of the nation's Gross National Product (GNP), we are playing with economic fire and likely to get badly burned. Governments generally don't run large segments of any society efficiently. Stop to think for a moment about the impact of government measures such as the "war on poverty." Since Lyndon Johnson's famous 1964 State of the Union address, rather than conquering poverty, we have come to subsidize and legitimize it. Making poverty comfortable enough that some people prefer to live in poverty than face the hard work to get out of it is a tragic mistake. As a result of misaligned incentives, this can continue for generations. The Affordable Care Act was another attempt to see if a government takeover of healthcare could result in something better. The result, unfortunately, may be the lowest common denominator rather than a healthcare system that is the envy of the world.

For all of our politicians' pompous statements on the "failure" of American healthcare, this is still the country that the majority of people in the world would come to if given the chance in the face of serious illness. This doesn't excuse the profound weaknesses in the current system, but it does hopefully give us pause to consider that hasty actions are not very likely to cure chronic problems. Even now, these challenges are not clearly understood by the power brokers in our nation's elected assemblies.

HEALTHCARE ACCESS AND LIFESTYLE CHOICES

If we are serious about healthcare reform, then let's look initially at the issue of what health is. Is it merely the absence of disease? What is disease? Is obesity a disease? Clearly it is, but sometimes it is a choice. It may not be a conscious choice, but it often is the result of many small lifestyle choices. Far better to address these behavioral choices early in obesity's onset than figuring out how to pay billions of dollars for hypertensive treatments, secondary diabetes, or lap band surgeries necessary in the future if we don't see a reversal of the national trend toward obesity. Health is profoundly impacted by lifestyle choices.

It is true that some lung cancers occur in those who have never smoked and have never been in the immediate environment of smokers for prolonged periods of time. It is also true that the vast majority of lung cancer sufferers have been long-term smokers. Looking at issues such as paying for health insurance and how these costs are handled, we need first to understand the purpose of insurance and then focus on what lifestyle choices cause disease.

Insurance is, by definition, the promise of reimbursement in the case of loss, paid to people or companies so concerned about hazards that they have made prepayments to an insurance company to cover those losses. One of the first things learned during the training to become a licensed agent is that insurance is designed to cover unexpected or unanticipated major losses. We don't take out insurance to cover oil changes for the car because it is known in advance that regular oil changes are required and the cost of them is manageable.

By the same understanding, it is a complete fallacy to talk about having insurance in case you get a cold or a headache. Everyone gets colds or headaches from time to time, and everyone will get well from these without any major interruption to their life or lifestyle. Now, could a headache be the first sign of something much more significant? Absolutely! That is why we insure against the catastrophic thing that we cannot plan for. However, we all must plan for the inevitable things that are going to happen to each of us.

What happens when some people choose not to plan, or want to plan ahead but are not financially able to do so? Questions like these have no easy answers. How do we help the person who is too poor to buy the most basic health insurance policy?

When we explore who should pay for what in the healthcare world, we are primarily dealing with philosophical issues rather than black-and-white moral issues. When we say that "the government" should pay for everyone's healthcare, what we are also saying is that it is acceptable for patients to be completely separated from the costs of their care, which takes away all incentives for individuals to take personal responsibility for their own health. Is it right to consign the costs of healthcare for all to the taxes of the few? Likewise, when we adamantly insist that everyone must cover their own healthcare costs, whatever happens to them, we may be missing the fact that no one wants to be ill and that many illnesses do not have any clearly definable preceding adverse lifestyle choice.

Anyone who has worked in family medical practice will tell you that there are always going to be those who can't pay their medical bills or who can't afford the prescription drugs that they need.

HEALTHCARE AND PERSONAL RESPONSIBILITY

Much of what happens in healthcare is a personal choice. The question that we must ask ourselves is who is being held responsible for those choices. It is a well-known fact that even though auto insurance is compulsory, there are still large numbers of people who choose to drive without any coverage. There were times in my student days, and in my early days as an immigrant in this country, when cash was very tight, and I couldn't afford fully comprehensive collision and theft coverage. Yet I always chose to at least take the minimum coverage demanded by law to protect the other driver and his or her property, even if that left me without enough money to cover my own vehicle.

It is not dissimilar with health insurance. We would all love fully comprehensive coverage, preferably paid for by someone else (our employer/our government/anyone but ourselves), but at the end of the day, the choices inevitably come back to us. If my employer pays my health insurance, then I don't get that income (i.e., cost of my health-care) in my paycheck. If the government pays the total cost of care (e.g., Medicaid and various other state and local programs), this again impacts me in the form of less take-home pay—it is now removed as a hidden tax.

Healthcare poses many such dilemmas. My neighbor may be infertile through no fault of her own. But does that make it my responsibility to cover the spiraling costs of her trying to have a baby with various expensive medical procedures? This question is even more cogent when we look at pregnancy as a choice with known medical costs. Similar issues abound throughout the world of medical care. Young men pay more than older men for car insurance because they don't drive as safely. Or look at riding motorcycles (and, in this country, being allowed to do that without a helmet) and ask who should be paying for putting that person back together after a traffic accident. All of our taxes cannot cover the costs of people's personal choices that lead to poor health outcomes. The challenges of healthcare are not always easy questions to answer. In any pluralistic society, there is plenty of room for disagreement. The problems come when we force our preferences on others by law.

So how do these philosophical questions apply to health insurance? It does seem appropriate, in a caring society, to set some minimum standard of healthcare that we want all citizens, and perhaps even non-citizens, to be able to access without fear of being turned away. When you agree to such an approach, however, you also have to agree on how it is going to be paid for. Not even the government can forever mandate something without making provisions for the costs of its mandates. In the very statement that some people are going to be provided a service for "free," we recognize that this means others will necessarily have to pay more. These costs, whether through increased taxes or through some form of cost shifting, are going to land at someone's door. At some point, the "someone" (those who are paying the bills) may decide they are not willing to carry the burden of those who are provided the free service. This is the de facto position in many parts of the country where some doctors will not accept any more Medicaid or Medicare patients because they fear the impact on their bottom line.

Some may ask whether doctors are really losing money or just not making much on these types of patients. In Chapter 5, I will tell Dr. Keith Smith's story, and it will be clear that he was being massively underpaid within the Medicare system. That is not always the case, but it is a challenge in many specialty areas. The result? Doctors then find they have to shift the costs to other patients. How is that fair?

How do we reconcile these opposing views? This brings me back to the central thesis of this book: Most ordinary people, those who make up the backbone of America, want to be compassionate and help where genuinely needed, but we also want everyone to carry primary responsibility for their own lives and actions. Are there answers within the free market, in the imaginations of those willing to try new approaches, that can move us toward a more balanced position for handling medical costs?

CHRISTIAN MEDICAL COST-SHARING PROGRAMS

As I described at the beginning of this book, my journey into trying to understand medical costs here in America was triggered by my knee injury. The reason I felt so strongly that these bills that I was being asked to pay were so outrageous was because of how I had chosen to protect myself from catastrophic medical bills. Relatively soon after arriving in America, I came across some Christian groups where members were literally sharing in each other's medical bills. The idea intrigued me, a practical application of the early Christian concept of "bearing one another's burdens." Apparently, the early Christian communities that were functioning in a hostile environment found themselves effectively needing to take care of each other. In one account (Acts 4:34), "There were no needy people among them because those who owned land or houses would sell them and bring the money to the apostles to give to those in need."[3] This sharing tradition has been followed for centuries, whether by the early Christians as described in Acts, by Catholic monks in the Middle Ages, or by Mennonite and Amish communities in the modern day. In many ways, this has been a foreshadowing of the sharing economy. Whether it is sharing a car (Uber) or opening up your home (Airbnb) or sharing in medical bills (GoFundMe and the emerging medical cost-sharing models), it is clear that sharing is here to stay.

Being a member of one of these groups, it just seemed wrong to me to ask the community to share in what I understood to be outrageously priced bills. If I had known then what I know now, I would have been even more outspoken about the need for pricing transparency and no surprise billing. These are not so much political issues as moral issues. My response in 1996 on receiving these bills was to challenge my own bills and to reach out to the Christian sharing community that I was a part of to offer to negotiate medical bills for others in the community. Before I knew it, The Karis Group was up and running and saving this community millions of dollars. Needing to handle a growing volume of negotiations, I began to organize this simple idea into a formal business plan. Over the years, The Karis Group became a recognized leader in medical cost containment. Alongside the bill negotiation, we learned how to navigate people through the complexities of the medical system. In those early days of this work, it was typical that the cash pay patient was charged many multiples of what those who had insurance or government payment plans had to pay. Why on earth would those offering cash at the time of service be paying much more than those whose payments were going to be delayed because of the third-party payer system that was then the norm? In every other area where we buy things, cash is King! What would it take for hospitals and clinics to understand that they should treat the cash payer as their favorite patient? Karis has grown through the years and is now led by my son, Matt, who has transformed the company into a SaaS (software as a service) company, now called Point Health, that is developing an app to make medical cost containment easily available to all.

Having negotiated hundreds of millions of dollars for the Christian medical cost-sharing ministries and having also gained much experience helping various insurance companies with similar negotiations, I understood that you could find common-sense solutions that could be applied with huge cost savings right across the whole of the healthcare spectrum.

First, these Christian ministries don't actually "cover" any medical incident. Instead, they use a noninsurance approach to enable members of their healthcare sharing communities to literally share each other's medical bills. Secondly, these groups generally don't handle the cost of small medical bills. It makes no more sense to share, or for that matter to insure, small medical bills than it does to insure tire repairs for our cars. Members of these sharing programs understand this approach does not shift personal responsibility for one's bills to someone or something else. Rather, it is providing a non-insurance approach to share large medical bills with a large number of others who are equally committed to such a creative solution.

Now don't just cancel your health insurance and rush out to join these healthcare sharing ministries. They may not accept you. You need to be a Christian, a regular churchgoer, and you have to agree in writing not to make certain lifestyle choices. Wait a minute, you may say, "That is just being self-righteous." Well, no, this is a determination based on solid empirical evidence, and it does lead to significantly lower health-care costs. So why shouldn't others, say those who have chosen a vegan lifestyle, set up their own comparable sharing programs? They might agree within their group that no one can eat meat, or smoke, or be more than 20 pounds overweight. With just a few of those simple measures, any group could hugely cut its healthcare costs.

Sadly, such creative approaches have been severely limited by the ACA. Only the few faith-based initiatives in existence on December 31, 1999, have been given exemptions to operate in this fashion. Why not leave open these creative ideas to any groups willing to work within similar community environments? Will Congress regulate innovation out of the picture even before the story begins?

These ideas may be pretty radical by depending on people's basic integrity rather than the power of the law. Shouldn't all of us be able to participate in these common-sense approaches that dramatically lower medical costs? Instead, we seem to be rushing without thought toward another trillion dollars of deficit spending, pushing us as a nation further into debt and ultimate poverty.

In 2011, as I was beginning to understand the potential impact of the recently passed ACA, I began talking with some of the leaders of the healthcare sharing ministries. Did they have any desire to expand their reach to help others outside of the Christian community? Would their sharing methodology work outside the limits of the evangelical Christian world?

But there was a problem. Even if you believed, as I did, that this methodology could work with any group of people, the exemption provided to Christian groups in the ACA was very narrowly scripted. The exemption included only those few groups that could show that they had been in existence since the end of 1999 and that their members shared a common religious foundation. Clearly, the government did not want any more of these groups, and it seemed that the Christian ministries were equally happy with a restricted exemption limiting competition. Either way, this government involvement was clearly going to actively restrict the impact of the free market.

By early 2014, my research showed a way to legally start a medical cost-sharing entity. It would not be protected by the ACA, but it wasn't disqualified from existing, either. Available court cases surrounding the Christian healthcare sharing ministries showed that the courts did not view them as insurance entities as long as they never accepted a transfer of risk from the member to the ministry. This had come into focus in two court cases that went to different state-level Supreme Courts.[4]

I mention these cases because they were featured prominently in shaping my own thinking as I tried to understand how to take the healthcare sharing methodology into the mainstream. In early 2012 I had begun meeting with a small group of people to try to help the Christian sharing ministries expand their work to include all people, not just people of faith. But, to my surprise, I found resistance to this idea.

I was strongly committed to the idea that when God blesses the Christian community with an approach that is clearly working, we should share it with all. However, most of the others felt that approach was naïve, and that a sharing approach would only work with people committed to a "Christian lifestyle." But in my thinking the Bible is clear: "Therefore, as we have opportunity, let us do good to all people, especially to those who belong to the family of believers" (Galatians 6:10).[5]

My understanding is that the goodness of God is there to bless all people. Jesus, commenting on an example from the life of Elisha in the Old Testament, noted that in Elisha's prayer for the healing of Naaman, a Syrian military commander, God was happy to heal someone who was not a Jew. Would not the same principles come into play with the healthcare sharing ministries being open to all? But I was clearly in the minority.

ENTREPRENEURIALISM IN HEALTHCARE AND THE START OF SEDERA

Entrepreneurs think differently than other people. We like to think outside of the box. Maybe it would be more accurate to say we wonder who created the box in the first place. Who wants to be confined to a box? It is not an idea that makes the entrepreneur. Ideas are a dime a dozen; ask any venture capitalist. If you want someone to invest in your idea, make sure that you can first show them what you have already been able to create. What sets the entrepreneur apart is the willingness to act on the idea, to risk everything for the idea. Most entrepreneurs fail at something before they learn how to execute. It's in building the team and being willing to try and fail that a great idea is birthed.

I love the way that many from Silicon Valley are challenging us to expand our thinking. Writers like Dr. Peter Diamandis, founder of the XPrize, describe this approach as having a Massively Transformational Purpose (MTP). The bigger the challenge, the bigger the reward. He and others like him are challenging entrepreneurs to dare to imagine a world of abundance, a world where the biggest problems are our biggest opportunities. Healthcare in America is a huge problem and a huge opportunity. Across the healthcare landscape, entrepreneurs are already demonstrating remarkable, workable, scalable answers. My question was whether I could create something that would transform our dependence on the insurance industry. Could we really find a better way? I knew in my heart it was better to fail grandly than not try at all. Sedera was my answer. Why not build on the model of the healthcare sharing ministries, but deliberately craft this as a mainstream solution, open to all, not just people of faith, wherein the employee could make their own choice as to whether they preferred the non-insurance voluntary sharing approach to an insurance model for handling large bills? From this early seed, Sedera would slowly emerge as an eminently workable idea.

It amazes me to see where we have come over the past six and a half years. In the Fall of 2020, at the Austin Business Journal Fast 50 Awards, we learned that we were the second-fastest growing company in Central Texas in the large company category. That same year, we found ourselves on the Inc. 5000 List for the first time, remarkably in the top 200. In April of 2021, the Financial Times (of London) announced that Sedera was #23 in their "Americas' Fastest Growing Companies 2021." Only a quality team can make all of this come together so quickly.

What I am describing here is just the start—we have hardly begun our journey of transformation. Sedera is little more than a blip on the radar screen of the entire healthcare industry. Actually, if that radar screen includes the various state departments of insurance that we work with around the country, then it would be fair to say that regulators keep us busy. But even here we are grateful. As the regulators do their job to keep consumers safe, we are finding that most are open to understanding that it is innovation that brings change. We decided early on in this process that the regulators are our friends. They want people provided for just as much as we do, and it is their job to make sure that nobody gets ripped off in the process. Transparency is just as important for us, as a medical cost-sharing organization, as it needs to be for the medical providers and insurance companies that have caused so many problems in the first place. If we want to hold others to a high standard, we must be prepared to hold ourselves to an even higher standard. An MTP demands sustainable answers, scalable answers, and answers that are consistent with best business practices.

When we started Sedera in 2014, we knew that we had massive hurdles to overcome. The Affordable Care Act had apparently made our plans impossible. People, by law, had to have insurance. Sedera is not insurance. This is where the entrepreneur refuses to accept the concept of "impossible." There must be a way. After all, companies all over the country were struggling to come to terms with the impact of the ACA. Watching those companies struggle gave me an idea.

The newspaper was reporting that one of the big steel companies was asking the IRS whether a "skinny plan" that just dealt with Minimum Essential Coverage (an MEC plan as described in the ACA) would fulfill the legal requirement that larger companies had to provide coverage to their employees. Initially, answers were not clear. But slowly, answers began to emerge. And in my mind a plan was emerging.

If the MEC plan did fulfill part A of the law's requirements (known generally as the individual mandate with its individual penalty), and a MEC plan was only dealing with preventative care, such a plan might be relatively cheap. Research showed that most major medical plans allocate only 5% or less of premium cost to preventative care. Maybe we could help companies find a self-insure MEC plan that would take care of their Part A requirements under the ACA and couple that with non-insurance medical cost-sharing to handle larger medical costs for their employees.

But for some employees, for whom an insurance plan would be a better solution, if the company also made available what the ACA describes as a Minimum Value Plan (MVP), that would also deal with the Part B penalties against the company, which were only incurred if a company chose not to provide an insurance plan as mandated in the law.

In 2014, we couldn't bring individuals into a medical cost-sharing approach because that would not have been in compliance with the ACA. Individuals would only be exempted from the Individual Mandate Penalty under the ACA if they joined one of the exempted ministries. We were not that, so we could not yet open our doors to individuals. It was this thinking that made us understand that, to get Sedera off the ground, we would have to begin by working with companies and their employees.

The fact that we could see a possible route to legitimately offer Sedera to companies did not mean that our challenges were over. When you have a big idea, you had better expect big obstacles, or you may be tempted to give up when those obstacles come. And come they have. The first thing we had to do was find some companies that were willing to risk their reputations with their employees. Would employees feel that their company was just trying to save money and give them fewer valuable benefits? What company is going to risk a completely new approach to handling something as important as healthcare for their employees? Naturally, every company would want to know whether this approach was legal. Would it prevent penalties under the ACA? Would Sedera even have enough money to handle medical bills using this new sharing approach?

Every one of these questions is totally appropriate. The uncertainties of what we were offering were top of mind for all of us as we pored over our basic assumptions and tried to rationalize asking people to trust us in such an important area. Time and again we explored every possible contingency. What if we faced a really large medical bill in our early months? How would we handle that cost? Knowing that this was a real possibility, some of us who were completely convinced that we were on a path that God had led us to decided that we would put our own money at risk by lending it to the medical cost-sharing community if such a challenge actually emerged.

God was good to us. In our first seven months we did not have even one person who asked for a medical need to be shared. In the six and a half years since then, tens of millions of dollars have been shared, and community funds have always been sufficient to handle any and every need, whatever its size. The difference between presumption and faith in the Christian walk is often the reality of having skin in the game and being willing to totally accept the consequences of our own choices and actions.

I could fill further chapters with the many other issues, large and small, that have faced us so far in this journey. That is not the purpose of sharing my own journey, however. I share my journey to say that if you have a goal that is big enough, it is worth risking everything to reach that goal. For me, pursuing this goal is a part of my call as a Christian committed to being a world changer.

It is useful to understand certain principles on the modern entrepreneurial journey. As you join me in understanding the power of an MTP, you will find that there are recurring themes for many who choose this road. Let's explore three key facets that lead to explosive growth.

The first facet of any MTP is the word Massive. What is so big about the idea that it is worth the risk of chasing after it? In our case, the answers were clear. Whatever is wrong with the current system, it is breaking the nation's financial backbone. Pay increases have virtually ceased for most employees over the past 10 to 20 years because the necessary money is being gobbled up by an increasingly expensive medical system. We have to show people a better way. And I had already seen this better way while working for those few people who knew about and had joined the exempted healthcare sharing ministries. If they could take the risk to begin with a few people back in the late 1980s, we could take the risk now to begin with a few companies. The most challenging part of dealing with inertia is getting started. Understanding the numbers can help.

There is a fable about an Indian emperor who was famous throughout the land for his ability at chess. The emperor made a proclamation offering anyone in his empire a fortune if they could beat him at chess. Many people tried, but no one succeeded. One day, a very poor peasant heard about this contest and decided he had to try to win.

On the day of the chess match, there was great excitement. Many had heard of the poor man's incredible skills. The game came to a stunning ending, with the poor peasant checkmating the emperor. The emperor stood up, acknowledged his loss, and offered the poor peasant one of two choices for his prize. He could have one large sack of rice for each square on the chessboard, or 64 sacks of rice, each requiring a cart and oxen to carry it back to the poor man's home. What a fortune this would represent! Or, if the poor man preferred, he could have one grain of rice for the first square, two grains of rice for the second square, and four grains of rice for the third square, doubling the grains of rice on each square until the 64th square. Which would the poor man prefer? Without hesitation, the poor man said, "I will take the one grain on the first square, doubling on each square until the 64th square." Smart choice. This would equal the number 18 with 18 zeros after it for the 64th square, or more than all of the rice in India.

This fable describes exponential growth. The rice doubled with every square. This is Moore's Law of computing: The number of transistors incorporated in a chip will approximately double every 24 months, while the cost will halve in the same period of time. Amazingly, this observation has held true for roughly 50 years. Modern authors note that, in the world of ideas, anything that can be digitized can also follow Moore's Law. An idea, such as medical cost-sharing, when reduced to ones and zeros, can spread like wildfire. The key is in understanding the early growth. Sedera started with three brave companies that were willing to risk letting us help them with their staff health costs. On January 1, 2015, these three companies represented approximately 100 employees. By January 1, 2016, we had 15 companies, representing approximately 300 employees. These numbers are so small that they make us look completely irrelevant! But, by doing a little more than doubling each year, by January 1, 2021, only five years later, our sharing community included more than 30,000 people. And the growth continues. If you have a big enough vision, an MTP, then it appears that almost anything is possible. Even change in the healthcare system!

Change on a big enough scale is transformation. Transformation, the second fact of an MTP, is our goal here. Better is not enough. The result needs to be different. It is not the old, gently improved; rather, it is new. Transformation is the result of a purpose that is bold. It is not enough to just want change. You must plan for that change. You "begin with the end in mind." Did Jeff Bezos begin with the thought that it would be great to sell books? I doubt it. My presumption is that he saw books as a stepping stone to selling everything else. Start where you are with what you can. Have the courage to keep pressing on. As a passionate follower of Christ, it is natural for me to believe as the Bible teaches me, "Now to him who is able to do immeasurably more than all we ask or imagine, according to his power that is at work within us."[6]

This creative power within us is able to surmount the greatest challenges around us. This is the call of the entrepreneur, whether it is my 10-year-old grandson with his neighborhood power washing business, or a world-class pulmonologist, such as Dr. Geetinder Goyal, who decides he can bring more transformation to the system by taking the risk of pioneering a direct primary care practice in Houston than by staying within the professional safety of his pulmonary specialty practice.

The stories so far have nearly all been about doctors, and that is natural because I am a doctor. I love learning about what other doctors are doing. But let me add one story here about a friend who works within another area of healthcare.

Clint Phillips played rugby professionally. Don't mess with this guy when it comes to sports. But his love of sports was a platform that led to training as a chiropractic and physical therapist at the University of Johannesburg, South Africa. Emigrating to the United States with his family opened the door to more rugby and to a desire to help people dealing with pain. His growing practice in Aspen, Colorado, was soon bringing people from all over the world. But in the middle of all of this success, a deep concern was growing.

Clint and Jade's young daughter, Gabi, was four months old and not moving the right side of her body normally. As would any concerned parents, they took their daughter to their pediatrician, who referred them to a specialist. But the specialist was not able to help either. The frustration and the worry of the next few years led to the idea for a company called 2nd.MD. And the rest of that story has become history, providing hundreds of thousands of people the help they needed from the most qualified doctors in the country with a second opinion service. This access to high quality care, as part of a medical plan, also dramatically reduces overall costs for the patient and their employer by cutting out all sorts of unnecessary care and making sure that treatments are completely up to date as recommended by specialists.

Not content with 2nd.MD's amazing success, Clint has gone on to found Medici. This brilliant idea is providing doctors with the tools they need to bring innovation to their practice of medicine. It is not so much that they are providing the family doctor with a better stethoscope. Rather, with the power of modern technology and communications, the family doctor can literally bring a cardiologist into the conversation with the patient on a virtual basis. Instant second opinions from specialists are literally what the doctor ordered. Clint and Jade were driven to get to the bottom of their daughter's illness. Every parent wants the best medical help for their kids.

These stories illustrate why we need to have a clear purpose, which is the third part of the MTP. Massive problems need bold answers. It is not enough to bring timid, incremental changes to a medical ecosystem that has lost its way. Some would say that after World War II, medicine took the following 75 years to be detached from its ethical and financial moorings, so it is okay if it takes us another 75 years to get back to something approaching solid foundations. If in the meantime this bankrupts us as a country, what do we do then? The accelerating nature of change in modern, technology-driven societies demands that we think in terms of an MTP.

USING PRICE INCENTIVES TO CHANGE BEHAVIOR FOR BETTER HEALTH

If we are serious about tackling "national health," then we must look at the incentives that motivate individuals and companies, both public and private. What motivates people to go for medical help? One of my business colleagues likes to tell the following story.

While walking past a friend's front porch, I saw his dog squirming. "What's wrong with your dog?" I shout.

"He's lying on a nail," calls back my neighbor.

"Why doesn't he move?"

"It doesn't hurt enough yet!"

Ouch! But isn't that the truth? Why don't people quit smoking, or lose weight, or start to exercise regularly rather than just squirming on their "nail"? To put it plainly, it doesn't hurt enough yet.

Companies have experimented with a variety of incentives. For example, some charge smokers more for their share of health insurance costs because they end up costing the company significantly more. Will the extra $25 per month change behaviors? Not necessarily, but at least it begins to bring some accountability to those who are generating the costs. No one is forced to quit smoking, but everyone is encouraged to stop, whether by negative encouragement, such as by paying a higher employee portion of health insurance costs, or by positive encouragement, such as the company offering incentives to quit. When many Americans quit smoking, it makes a huge dent in the national health bill.

TAX AND POLICY IMPEDIMENTS TO BETTER HEALTHCARE SYSTEMS

On the other side of these issues, there are no incentives for major insurance carriers to cut their premium costs significantly by encouraging consumers or employee groups to switch to more affordable high deductible plans that are eligible for health savings accounts (HSAs). Such accounts have already been shown to help keep premium growth down and to significantly enhance customer participation in their own healthcare decisions. From an economic point of view, such plans make great sense. But from a profit point of view, it is better to make a monthly profit of 10 percent on a $1,000-per-month policy than 10 percent on a $500 policy. Why would any insurance company even consider promoting a very effective $150-per-month product, such as some limited benefit medical products, if it can persuade the consumer—or the government—that a $1,000 product is much better?

It is true that you will probably have much more coverage on a $1,000 insurance product than you will have on a $150 product. But if the choice, as is currently the case, is between either the $1,000 product or nothing, then everything changes. Similarly, why should the fit and healthy 25-year-old have to cover the cost (not just this year, but in an escalating fashion for the next 40+ years) of the unhealthy 25-year-old smoker? They both make choices, and currently neither has much by way of incentives, except possibly for the fit 25-year-old to opt out of health insurance altogether. Now even that option has been effectively removed or at least penalized by law. We need to learn how to apply incentives in such a way that people do not have to be coerced into choices that are good for them and good for the public interest.

The current tax code favors those whose health insurance premiums are paid by their companies (a tax-deductible expense to the companies). A much more rational policy would be to remove that tax break. Every company would pay their employees their full wages rather than hiding much of the salary in "benefits." Then make all health insurance premiums tax deductible. There are strong reasons for removing the tax break altogether because it currently favors those in higher tax brackets more than those in lower tax brackets, but exploring this is beyond the scope of this book.

We could also bring incentives to the insurance companies themselves. Rather than putting an increasingly onerous burden of escalating taxes and mandates on these companies, the government could favor innovation and competition (which is a marvelous incentive to "keep up with the Joneses," even for companies) by expanding the role of HSAs.

The government could also encourage competition among providers by encouraging an environment in which competition can flourish. Current regulations tend to restrict new ideas such as specialty hospitals, even though these have been shown to be successful at cutting costs. As we watch the current growth of medical tourism that draws people to specialty hospitals abroad, it is hardly surprising that some American hospitals are now finding effective ways to provide local competition without the need to travel. Couldn't such trends be encouraged?

Public/private partnerships could also be encouraged to find innovative ways to help those whose healthcare is primarily provided through the public purse. Rather than squeezing out private competition by mandates and price controls, government can incentivize those on Medicaid to share responsibility for their own healthcare needs by allowing savings accounts, like HSAs, to remain the property of the recipient. If they are able and willing to manage their own healthcare dollars effectively, they can pocket the difference. If the money for care is coming out of the Medicaid recipient's HSA, they will probably quickly learn the difference between the cost (and convenience) of an emergency room at 11 p.m. and the cost of an urgent care clinic.

A few years ago, while my wife was visiting our oldest son's family, their eldest daughter came down with a weird condition causing joint pain and a peculiar rash. It was late at night, and Felicity was coming back to Texas the next day. Should the family go to the emergency clinic, or would it be alright to wait until morning? Well, as you know, Felicity and I are doctors, and our daughter-in-law was able to get our advice. Felicity was happy to watch things until morning. Our daughter-in-law was glad to have this decision aided by family via a phone consultation. The cost in the morning was just a couple of hundred dollars to see a great family doctor who recognized Henoch-Schonlein purpura. (All credit to this family doctor because it hadn't occurred to either Felicity or I; neither of us had ever seen a case of this disease before.) The family doctor did the necessary blood and urine tests. In contrast, an emergency room visit would probably have led to $2,000 to $4,000 for blood work, urine analyses, and X-rays, plus or minus an MRI.

Maybe everyone should have access to a telemedicine program like CallMD or Teladoc. What a great way to cut down unnecessary visits to the emergency room or get a medical second opinion. Hmmm . . . Why didn't I think of that as a business model first?

CHAPTER 5

WHILE YOU WERE SLEEPING

I N THE 1995 ROMANTIC COMEDY "While You Were Sleeping," Sandra Bullock plays a woman who is mistaken for the fiancée of a patient in a coma played by Peter Gallagher. Peter reminds me of so many of us within the medical community who have been similarly "comatose" within the world of medical economics.

Most of us find ourselves in a figurative coma when it comes to thinking about our healthcare system. We passively accept the way things are. And yet, we all have a personal responsibility to try to change the system, whether as healthcare providers, consumers of healthcare, or especially as business owners providing health insurance to employees that is so expensive that we can't afford to give employees the pay raises we want to give. We all need to be part of the transformation of the system.

Dr. Keith Smith is a welcome antidote to the lack of observation that allows so many in the medical system to unwittingly become a part of the problem rather than a part of the answer.

DR. SMITH AND THE SURGERY CENTER OF OKLAHOMA

Dr. Keith Smith, founder of the Surgery Center of Oklahoma, began his journey to fair pricing back in the 1990s, when he began to appreciate that the vows he took as a physician demanded that he stop participating in the system. In this way, he could withdraw his consent to what was going on. What did he mean by this? By the late 1990s, Medicare had begun drastically cutting payments to anesthetists for the services they provided. Incensed by this, he could see no reason to accept the value that the government was putting on his work. The complex services provided during a five-hour cardiac case might net him, as an anesthetist, less than $300 in a Medicare case. This seemed absurd! Why would he play along with this drastic undervaluing of the service he was providing? He decided that he would rather just treat the Medicare patient for free, making a voluntary choice to be a blessing to his patients, and then find a way to make a living by creating a new kind of healthcare operation. At his new Surgery Center of Oklahoma, he would let patients know up front what the costs were and charge them directly for his services.

There are two ways to make an exchange of value. You can do this voluntarily, by a mutually valued exchange as takes place in a free market, or you can make an exchange under coercion when forced to accept the government or insurance company "price" that is offered. For Dr. Smith, it was liberating to walk away from a system that under-valued him and make his skills and knowledge available to people who chose to use his services for a reasonable cost. He quickly discovered that he could consistently provide patient services for less than the cost of the deductible under an insurance plan. Why should the patient pay a high premium and then face a deductible where their out-of-pocket minimum is still more than the total cost of all aspects of the surgery in many cases?

In 1997, after opening the Surgery Center of Oklahoma with a small group of surgeons and anesthetists who understood and shared Dr. Smith's passion for a mutual exchange of value, the practice set transparent prices that, for the most part, have not changed in 20 years. In fact, in many cases they have been able to bring the pricing down still further. All of their prices for every aspect of the surgery (surgeon, anesthetist, hospital facility, etc.) are published on the web. This is known as bundled pricing, and there are no hidden fees and no gotchas. Just an open, voluntary exchange of value.

Appreciating the value of the free market opens the door for normal market forces to shape the exchange of value in the medical context. Examples of this abound in medicine, just as they do in other, more transparent examples of the free market. I was recently asked by a friend what I thought of the price a hospital proposed for his daughter's needed ankle surgery. He was being quoted $9,500, and he was responsible under his insurance plan for a $5,000 deductible. Did this price seem fair? I called the hospital and asked for their cash price. They quoted me $3,500, but this did not include surgeon and anesthetist fees. Checking online with a local surgery center, where there are no hidden or extra fees, the same procedure was $2,950. Let the free market set the pricing!

Talking with Dr. Smith is like a light being turned on in a dark room. Suddenly you can see. "Medicare is a Ponzi scheme," he told me. When it started in 1965, Medicare was founded by people with a reasonable desire to help the elderly. The economists who advised them imagined that a moderate tax on 20 working people would drastically cut the financial pressure on one elderly person who depended on those taxes to pay his or her medical bills. But times have changed. Now, there are about three working people for each person receiving Medicare. Everyone knows, and even the government acknowledges, that the Medicare Trust Fund is now expected to run out in 2024.[1] Neither political party has yet shown the moral courage, let alone the economic common sense, to find a way to reform this inevitable disaster.

Again, as Dr. Smith has explained in our conversations, "Coercion is inherent in a single-payer system." Whether it is the government or insurance companies, you see a similar result. Costs go up, administrative layers and regulations proliferate, and the relationship between the patient and the doctor is relegated to a lesser position. But the doctor–patient relationship is what enables us to see the way forward.

Dr. Smith is really clear in what he is telling us. His willingness to walk away from the system was his way of declaring his own value. Why should the government declare his value by forcing him to accept something way below market value for his services? He came to realize that he was not only devaluing his own worth but was also effectively complicit in the financial crimes being perpetrated on patients at the most vulnerable moments in their lives. Feeling morally compromised by operating within a system that did not allow him to put the best interests of his patients first was not something that he could live with. He knew everything was going to have to change. He needed to act in accordance with what he believed.

In 1990, when he started his practice, he felt that he was paid fairly. But by 1992, when the government had become actively involved in limiting anesthetist income through what is known as Harvard's Resource Based Relative Value Scale, he knew that he was being turned into a slave to the system. In 1990, he received approximately $1,000 for a complicated cardiac case, but now the government was saying he would receive only $500. By 1993, when round two of this approach was implemented by the government, his payment was reduced to $285 for a complex six-hour procedure. Keith understood that the government was signaling the value it placed on Keith's contribution to his patients' health. If he wanted to maintain his independence, then he had to send a signal back. So, he did. He quit!

In a normal market economy, price controls produce shortages. Keith understands this. His decision was not emotional but active. To stop working with the government while still caring for the Medicare patients that the hospital wanted him to serve, he stopped filing claims but continued to look after the patients. He was not willing to legitimize the system by having the government decide his value. Instead, he began thinking through how he would let patients know what he did, what he charged for this service, and that it was then up to the patient if they valued the service enough to pay for it. What emerged out of this was the Surgery Center of Oklahoma.

This intellectual journey of understanding economics is, in Keith's words, "the study of human behavior." Books like *Atlas Shrugged* by Ayn Rand and *The Law* by Frédéric Bastiat were by now beginning to shape his thinking. His parents, both highly academic and very left wing in their thinking, had decided to travel to Moscow in the late 1970s to see what an ideal society could look like. They were so shocked and disappointed by all that they saw that, upon their return, they embarked on a journey to understand what was making America so prosperous. Keith joined in. These books were a part of that journey.

This understanding of economics has led to some amazing outcomes. When Keith and his colleagues set the prices for procedures being done at Surgery Center of Oklahoma in 1997, they had little experience in how to do so fairly. But seeking to establish a fair price for the patient and a fair reward (payment) for the doctor was foundational to his thinking. Yet these prices are normally less than half of those for identical procedures done in other hospitals within Oklahoma City. How is this possible?

One thing that has facilitated this is the concept of "the bundle." When they quote a price for gallbladder removal or for knee replacement, the price they quote is the complete price including surgery, anesthesia, labs, surgical implant, and so on. There is no surprise billing here. You know the full cost of everything, all in, before you start. Patients and doctors love this approach. And this approach has a staggering impact on the administrative and overhead costs experienced in other hospital systems. When Dr. Smith took me for a tour of their facility, I could hardly believe that the space for administration and billing was almost nonexistent. Staff members are focused on quoting prices for procedures and setting up surgery appointments. There is no need to worry about accounts receivable and collections when everyone pays at the time they are seen, and no insurance paperwork is necessary.

The market has pushed Dr. Smith and his team to find greater efficiencies, and vendors have been willing to reduce prices as they watch the incredible work being done by the Surgery Center of Oklahoma. During the past 20 years, while others have been doubling their prices, the Surgery Center of Oklahoma has dramatically "lowered" what they are actually charging in real dollars because of the impact of inflation. Keep in mind that the surgeons who work at the Surgery Center of Oklahoma are actually paid more than they receive at any of the other facilities where they work, even though prices are much higher at those other facilities. This is the power of the free market bringing greater efficiencies into the whole process of surgical care at this remarkable surgery center. By being willing to do away with profitability on the institutional side of the Surgery Center (i.e., making money just from owning the facility), one of the largest components of profits being generated at most hospitals is removed in one stroke. Currently, these "facility charges" are often worse at so-called nonprofit hospitals, which

WHILE YOU WERE SLEEPING • 77

are not only the most likely to sue their own patients for nonpayment but are also the most likely to engage in price gouging with facility charges.

THE NEED FOR TRANSPARENCY

When the goal is not maximum revenue but maximum value, this changes everything. The free market naturally provides a strong incentive to all who take part to let the market keep them both transparent and honest. This helps to underscore the importance of the transparency movement that has gained such momentum since former president Trump's mandate. It was Dr. Smith's outrage at the sense that he was participating in a system that was like a financial serial killer (his words) to his patients that prompted him to make sure that all pricing at the Surgery Center of Oklahoma would be transparent, clear, and demonstrate great value.

There are two basic systems of exchange: One is economic, and one is political. An economic exchange naturally follows the Golden Rule to "do unto others as you want them to do unto you." This is voluntary and works best when viewed by both parties as a win-win, even though this process has been subverted by the crony capitalism that permeates the health insurance system. In contrast to this, and where we see economics corrupted by government interference, is an exchange that is viewed by one party as a win and by the other party as a loss. When government uses the coercive power of taxation and regulation to take from one person to give to another, natural market forces tending toward transparency and creation of value disappear, and in their place, you have the situation where the government picks the winners and losers. When the government protects hospitals that already exist by saying that no more hospitals (or surgery centers) can be started in an area, it is destroying the power of the free market to keep costs down. The same is true when the government protects healthcare sharing ministries with an exemption that forbids other similar ministries or businesses from starting. The government's role is to ensure a level playing field for our entrepreneurial activities and protect the consumer.

Keith Smith has experienced more than his share of regulatory and institutional interference in his 20 years of pioneering at the Surgery Center of Oklahoma. When I asked him what it was like walking away from Medicare reimbursements back in 1993, he had this to say:

> I stopped accepting money from Medicare in 1993. I was three years into my practice. Any physician I know that has walked away from Medicare will tell you that is the most liberating event of their private practice . . . One of the reasons that I walked away was just not wanting to legitimize what I considered an illegitimate system, but I had come to realize that any payment that I received came from my neighbor's wallet for rendering service to someone across town my neighbor didn't even know. And the price I was paid, the money that I was paid, was probably affordable to that person who was across town. So again, I was part of the problem. I saw receiving Medicare funds as being the recipient of stolen property. That's how I looked at it. I saw it as much, much more awful than just a Ponzi scheme. The way that physicians can lead, can declare their place in the marketplace, is to be marketplace actors, to declare their pricing. Here is what I do and here is how much it is going to cost. This is how physicians step back into their proper role by becoming true marketplace actors and trying to maximize delivery of value, not trying to maximize the revenue.

When you hear the passion in Dr. Smith's voice as he articulates these ideas, it becomes clear that he never wants to be in a context where physicians are helping patients medically while destroying them financially.

A close friend of mine, Dr. John Hunt, Chief Medical Officer at Sedera, expresses very similar thoughts and feelings. He chose to give up his tenured position at a highly respected university hospital medical system. He could not and would not accept that it was appropriate to charge patients 3,000 percent more (yes, that is 30 times more) for lab work and other procedures than it cost the department to provide those services. When you see this type of dedication coming from many of the nation's physicians, you know there is hope for the medical system. When growing numbers of physicians say, "Enough is enough; I won't participate in stealing from my patients," then you know there is light at the end of the tunnel. Grassroots movements can suddenly explode through the power of ideas.

Physicians are beginning to learn that it is not enough to say they just want to practice medicine or to "leave the money side of this to other people." Instead, they are standing up to the system rather than abdicating their roles as patient advocates. As John Stuart Mill famously said, "All that is necessary for evil to triumph is for good men to do nothing."

Growing numbers of physicians are seeing the inherent challenges of working for the hospital or clinic rather than working for—and being paid by—the patient. At the very least, the passion that most doctors have for their work includes making sure that they don't harm their patients financially. For those willing to look at the things we are discussing here, it is clear that it is hard to argue with cheaper and better for both patient and doctor.

So why do insurance companies and hospitals fight what they see happening? The answer is actually pretty simple, and it is a clear example of how some of the big health insurance companies and providers have

corrupted the free market system in such a way that most people working in the system don't understand their role in what has gone wrong.
Or, if they do understand the system, they feel powerless to change it.
Hospitals and insurance companies make more money by not working
with places like the Surgery Center of Oklahoma. Insurance companies
prefer higher premiums because they get a percentage as profit of every
premium dollar. Patient Provider Organizations (PPOs) get paid on a
percentage of what they save. They want the "shared savings" to appear
much higher than they really are. This is a percentage off a fictional price
to start with. The system is fixed. And hospitals are often even worse, as I
describe in other parts of this book when recounting my own experiences
as a patient. Even Medicare gets in on this game. They usually pay double to the big hospital systems for a service provided by a surgeon who
is a hospital employee than they will to the same surgeon for doing the
same surgery in a surgery center. Hospitals then use this money to buy
up local medical practices and various other anticompetitive practices
to try to put independent physicians out of work. Anyone can see how
this system-wide bias is not only unethical but also actively immoral. In
some cases, even the insurance broker, who supposedly works for the
employer but is actually paid by the insurance company, joins in this
game by being paid a commission on the dollar amount of claims that
their customer is paying. And who pays for all of this? All of us do—in
our taxes, our medical bills, our insurance premiums, and in money that
does not show up in our paychecks.

It is really important to understand that all of us, as consumers,
have a responsibility to help change the system. We don't have to wait
for Washington to make decisions for us. We can vote with our feet.
We can make sure that we will only go to physicians who are open and
honest about their prices. We can refuse to be part of a system that is
designed to separate consumers from their money. As Timothy Snyder

wrote: "We would like to think we have healthcare that incidentally involves some wealth transfer; what we actually have is wealth transfer that incidentally involves some healthcare."[2]

Once we understand this, we can start becoming part of the answer rather than allowing ourselves to be part of the problem. As a doctor, I can resign from Medicare. I can post my prices. I can opt out of networks and be available to anyone who chooses to come to me. As a patient, I can make sure I only go to medical providers or facilities that are cash-friendly. As a business owner, I can make cash-friendly health plan options available to my employees and ensure that those options are the best for the employees and for my company's bottom line. As an insurance broker, I can adopt fee-only practices that are transparent and fair, where I am paid by the person I should be helping, namely my customers. As a third-party administrator (TPA), I can drop translucent practices that allow me to double dip by benefiting from vendor contracts and PPO repricing schemes that allow me to profit at the expense of the very people that I claim to serve.

As Dr. Smith explained to me, "Everybody has to do their part for there to be a market economy. There have to be willing buyers and willing sellers." We can be honest about what we charge, and we can openly demonstrate the value that we provide. People will always pay for great value. This is the ecosystem that is now developing all over the country as we work together toward the goal of open and honest medical cost transparency.

DR. DICKERSON AND GREEN IMAGING

Dr. Cristin Dickerson is doing her part to make this possible. Her focus has been on value for money through lower costs with greater access. As president of the Executive Committee of the Diagnostic Clinic of Houston from 1994 to 2007, she was well placed to see the impact of costs on her own clinic's health plan for their employees. Within her own specialty, radiology, she thought about what could be done to help even out the arbitrary way in which two employees with the same radiological needs might pay $3,000 at one facility and $300 at another. As she thought this through on behalf of the many groups, large and small, that the radiology group she founded served, the beginnings of an idea began to form. If a company like Travelocity or Priceline could use surplus capacity in the travel industry, could she find a way to bring that approach to radiology? And so Green Imaging was created.

The multi-specialty clinic where Dr. Dickerson was the CEO had been focused on bringing down the costs for its own self-funded health plan. Could she offer other self-funded employers a way of stabilizing the radiology portion of their medical costs? Surely other radiology units and clinics would be glad to rent out their staff and facilities for the portion of time that was surplus to their own requirements, leaving Dr. Dickerson and her team of radiologists to handle the highly technical side of reading these imaging results. Whether in a free-standing radiology unit or a hospital-based radiology department, most facilities could easily handle a greater workload. Having, perhaps, the time and resources on any given day to handle three more MRIs and five more CAT scans, why not rent out these technical resources to Green Imaging to provide patients to fill the available slots? This approach provides a win-win for everyone involved.

The ideas outlined here took several years to develop. Initially she started by incentivizing her own employees to use their own clinic facilities. This was a no-brainer and expanded quickly to encouraging her employees to also use various local strategic partners. At a time when premium costs were skyrocketing, her multi-specialty clinic was actually cutting the costs of employee healthcare. Then the idea came to her that since she and her team of radiologists were already reading the imaging for so many other imaging centers only working at 50–70 percent capacity, she might be able to buy the available spare capacity to help self-pay patients have access to imaging at significantly lower costs. This was so successful that it became clear to her that the employee groups their multi-specialty clinic worked for could also benefit from access to these discounted prices.

One should not assume that all went smoothly on this journey. Learning the legal and regulatory hoops that she needed to jump through was a complex and time-consuming task. Detours, such as working with networks and handling scheduling for members of those networks to have their imaging studies done, showed that not all patients had the same level of personal responsibility. Patients coming to them through ACA plans proved mainly unreliable. Internal studies demonstrated that they were spending four times as much on administration to handle members of these networks than they were on directly contracted self-pay and self-funded plan members. Slowly the pieces of this puzzle came together, including dropping the association with networks that could not deliver the types of patients she was looking for.

As Dr. Dickerson and I discussed this learning process, she emphasized the following: "I think the one thing we need to be careful about is not over-simplifying things because patients end up not getting the care they need. We need to be careful about throwing patients out there as consumers without guidance."

This is precisely where quality companies are beginning to spring up to help patients navigate some of the complexities of the medical world. The ideal situation is when the patient has a strong family doctor relationship, preferably through a direct patient care model of primary care. In this context, a doctor helps to quarterback the care of the patient. Add an app, such as that being developed by Point Health or through the Free Market Medical Association's ShopHealth Marketplace, that clearly provides the data to the consumer on the cost of care, and you have a winning combination.

In recent years, Dr. Dickerson's concept has taken off. Soon 100 outlets turned into 300, and now, nine years into this journey, they have more than a thousand locations scattered across 40 states. When one courageous pioneer launches an idea like this, soon 10 others who had similar ideas, but perhaps neither capital nor courage, will follow suit. Subsequently, the market identifies and sustains multiple entities similar to Green Imaging. We can picture this experimentation gaining momentum and spreading rapidly across the United States. Soon the type of price savings and convenience that Green Imaging offers through their many outlets will be available across the whole of the United States. This is the power of the market. A pioneer such as Dr. Dickerson provides a huge service to all others who have interest in following in her footsteps. Whether through sharing or licensing of her platform or challenging other radiologists to embark on such an entrepreneurial journey, the rising tide that she is creating really does help to raise all ships.

While asking Dr. Dickerson what she sees as some of the biggest gaps and challenges that we face in bringing these concepts to the market, she made some comments that focused on the heart and the mind of the entrepreneur. Her first thought was to start talking about others who are addressing these challenges. This was my first introduction to Dr. Juliet Breeze, whose remarkable work in creating Next Level Urgent Care centers across the Houston metroplex is going to capture part of our focus in the next chapter. But it's Dr. Dickerson's second point that we need to address here.

My husband and I have been guinea pigs on a lot of different, nontraditional insurance plans and we had a defined benefit plan last year. He ended up with kidney stones and I had to go get a stent placed and they couldn't retrieve it on the first try. [In spite of these incidents,] we figure that we have saved about $80,000 in the past three to four years by using these other types of insurance. We are moving around and seeing what we like. On the kidney stones we ended up with maybe a $30,000 bill and we negotiated it down to seven or eight thousand. He still had to go back and have the stone lasered and get the stone broken up and all that. We went in on a weekday that time and we were offered a $5,000 deal. And that would have been a $40–50,000 bill normally. I think hospitalization and acute care are still the issue.

The reason I quote their story here is not the size of the bills, but rather the huge savings over a period of a few years for a couple who were willing to engage directly in managing their healthcare costs. A recurring theme in the stories in this book is that when you choose to move into a cash-pay world, you can expect significant cash-pay savings. Everything is negotiable in medical care, and cash is king as in most other transactions within a transparent marketplace. Now, please don't belittle the skill and value of the physician or clinic that is offering a transparent cash-pay price. Do your research online, and if you are being offered a great price, don't nickel and dime the provider when you can instead be deeply appreciative of their pioneering role in bringing transparency and fair pricing to the marketplace. If you go to an emergency room, the paperwork they want you to sign will contain a statement, buried however deep, that you'll pay everything they charge you. In an emergency situation, like the one I will describe when I discuss more of my own experience with medical care later in this book, you have a right to emergency care without signing anything. You can demand the care first and then deal with any paperwork later, when you are in your right mind rather than transfixed by pain or, even worse, by the very drugs that will dull the pain but also remove your ability to understand all that you are signing.

Innovation and pricing transparency within specialty care is not limited to surgical and radiological specialties. As innovation works for doctors in one specialty, these ideas begin to grow and spread. That is the power of an idea. COVID-19 has also been a liberating influence for doctors as they understand the power of the remote consultation. Previously, I had to go for my own urological follow-up to the urologist's office. Now we just handle things remotely by phone. Without the travel, this saves me a lot of time. Maybe next time I speak with the urologist I will suggest to him that it should also save me money. After all, there were no other staff involved in my remote consultation.

Dr. Louis Flaspohler is a rheumatologist. He has been working closely with the family practice residency program in Cincinnati where he also has his practice. Already a leading expert in the area of "lean methodologies" in medicine, he has now widened his passion to helping doctors outside of the family practice arena understand the power of direct payment within specialty care. When approached by Dr. Diana Girnita, a rheumatology colleague moving to California because of her husband's recent appointment to a cardio-thoracic surgical unit there, Dr. Flaspohler was able to help her navigate the start-up of a remote rheumatology service for patients with chronic joint disease.

Dr. Bob Campbell is an anesthetist who is having a powerful impact in helping the medical profession understand why there are often (unnecessary) drug shortages. His research into the role of pharmacy benefit managers (PBMs) and the literally hundreds of billions of dollars a year they collect as middlemen protected by a federal safe-harbor law, while providing little if any value to the pharmaceutical supply chain, is a testimony to the dogged persistence of this medical warrior. He has done more than the whole of the American Medical Association (AMA) to expose the excessive and inexcusable profits of PBMs and their sister organizations, the Group Purchasing Organizations (GPOs), sheltering under safe-harbor laws that protect them from competition and racketeering charges that would follow if this was happening in any other industry.

Ideas can spread very quickly, as these stories show. Every part of medical care can adopt these ideas and the power of pricing transparency.

A NEW VISION:
BETTER ACCESS, HIGHER QUALITY, LOWER COSTS

Whether working with self-pay individual consumers or with self-funded companies that represent approximately 80 percent of all of the private claims paid for medical needs around the country, we need the pioneering work of people like these doctors to show us the way forward. When the employer wakes up, the employer, as the giant payer within the system, can transform the cost of medical care through normal market forces. First, CFOs and CEOs must wake up to the fact that medical costs are usually the number two or number three expense destroying their bottom line. They can reverse this by getting their company plans directly aligned with the emerging cash-pay ecosystem that is being described in this book. Now is the time to decide to bring this major area of company expenditure under the same financial controls already used for any other area of major expenditure. Don't just rely on your insurance broker any more than you would rely on any other outside consultant. You can and should take responsibility for changing how your company deals with healthcare costs.

CHAPTER 6

WE CAN DO BETTER

A REAL PLAN FOR HEALTHCARE is based on simple principles rather than complex and detailed rules (laws) and regulations. The political process sucks decision-making away from local, doctor–patient relationships and into the abyss of a Washington, D.C., world that is removed from everyday realities. This is the world where people who are not seeing patients, and for the most part have little if any medical knowledge, make decisions that often interfere with the people closest to the problems. This decision-making should primarily reside with doctors and their many and varied clinical colleagues and the patients they are striving to serve.

The starting point for putting together such a plan is understanding the foundational role of the doctor–patient relationship and the place of primary care in establishing this relationship. Don't think of a medical plan as something that you buy from insurance companies via a broker. Instead, begin to understand that a real medical plan is not a

45-page document, mainly filled with small print, but rather a simple, overarching description of how to provide:

- Better Access
- Higher Quality
- Lower Costs

This is a medical plan I could get behind. Whether I represent myself and my family, my companies, or our nation's economy, something this simple is a true example of what a medical plan needs to accomplish. If your basic plan design can't be outlined in one simple paragraph, it is probably not a plan but a continuation of the problem that most people are already stuck with. The K.I.S.S. principle comes into play here: Keep It Simple Stupid!

Notice that there is no mention of insurance here. Insurance is a part of the problem in the current situation. While insurance might be the best solution for some people or families, insurers must prove that they can consistently meet all three goals to be a comprehensive solution. I doubt that this will happen in my lifetime.

Enter direct patient care (known as DPC). This is the true foundation of any plan like the one I have described briefly above. When we know what we want to accomplish, and we are clear about why this is important, then we can move directly to how we can do this.

Direct primary care is a way of reclaiming the primacy of the relationship between the doctor and patient and reinstating the meaningful exchange of value between the two. Health insurance companies and all the other middlemen in the healthcare industry have destroyed this relationship, erected countless barriers to accessing medical care, and increased the costs to patients for care. At some level, most of the participants in this system have become resigned to passive acceptance. But it doesn't have to be this way.

What do we want to do? Let me reiterate: We want better access, higher quality, and lower costs.

Why are we doing this? Because we love our families, we love our employees, and we care about peoples' take-home pay. It matters to us that people all over the country are seeing their annual salary increases disappear into higher medical costs with lower benefits and no extra take-home pay.

I suspect I am biased, but I see quality primary care as the bedrock upon which the first leg of this three-legged stool—lower cost—is built. I am a family doctor, or what in England is called a general practitioner or GP. I guess I am a typical jack of all trades and master of none. None, that is, except for the ability to provide that core of medical care that comes from the doctor–patient relationship.

When medicine moved from the relational to the transactional, and particularly when the transaction stopped including any meaningful exchange of value in the form of money changing hands between patient and doctor, the doctor–patient relationship began to deteriorate. The imposition of the third-party payer, whether in the form of the benevolent employer providing a government-mandated "benefit" or the "kind" government providing us with a new "right," further destroyed the doctor–patient relationship. With the payer so far removed from the patient, the patient loses sight of cost. Once cost doesn't matter, quality tends to deteriorate, and prices inevitably escalate.

Now, I watch with delight, and a slight tinge of envy, as a whole movement is emerging, composed of primary care physicians (PCPs) who have taken on the system with their membership-based direct primary care practices.

DR. GROSS AND THE SHIFT TO DIRECT PRIMARY CARE

Movements begin in the most unlikely of places. In the early 2000s, a few doctors around the country were trying what was known as "concierge medicine," a very high-end, expensive way of providing excellent primary care and virtually unlimited access to the doctor. The very small number of patients who could afford this—basically the rich and the famous—received fabulous access and, usually, excellent care. From this seed, however, the plant that would become DPC grew and is now flourishing.

Dr. Lee Gross is one of the best-known figures within this new movement, but I can assure you his journey did not start on Easy Street. In talking with Dr. Gross about his early experiences in direct primary care, all sorts of interesting points emerge. In 2009, like virtually all primary care physicians, Dr. Gross was dealing with what he described as "the rat race of insurance-based fee for service primary care. We were playing this game of 'Whack-a-Mole' with Medicare . . . Every way we found to plug the leaks in our practice, due to over-regulation of the practice, Medicare found another way to chop out more from under us, yet again."

Dr. Gross and his practice were finding cheaper and easier ways to serve patients by bringing additional services in house, but Medicare didn't seem to want to compensate them for their innovations. In trying to understand why Medicare would do this, Dr. Gross began to learn more about the mysterious world of government-run medicine. He discovered that the issue was not that the government did not want the cheaper lab work or X-rays that his practice could offer. Instead, they didn't want the lab work or X-rays performed at all! When a government working on a fixed budget is handling the costs, the government inevitably tries to limit access to medical care as much as possible. In this respect, Medicare shared many of the same qualities as the Canadian system. If you have already run out of money, you need to control costs wherever possible. Medicare was limiting more and more what the doctor could do for the patient. This cost-containment was all taking place under the label of weeding out "fraud and abuse" or "overutilization." But what the government called "overutilization," their medical practice considered being stopped from practicing good medicine. Dr. Gross provides insightful comments looking back on this time:

> The behaviors that we were doing (now that I'm out of that model, the biases are just astronomical) I could never go back and do again, ever. What we kept saying at that period of time, and of course that was also the run up to the Affordable Care Act, we saw the writing on the wall that our practices were really about to be handed over as food to the insurance companies. We just couldn't fathom the fact that was going to be our fate. We kept saying there has to be a better way. What happened after that was just by pure accident!
>
> A small business owner in our community owned a heating and air conditioning company that had about ten employees. He came up to me and one of my colleagues and told me their insurance premiums were going up yet again. Since he, as the employer, saw the premiums and knew what our practice charged to see his employees, he was naturally asking, "Why am I paying them to pay you. And they keep almost all of the money when you are doing all of the work. Can't I just pay you directly to take care of my employees?"

That moment of revelation was Dr. Gross's epiphany, and this is why he calls his southern Florida practice Epiphany Health. Why were they allowing the insurance company to come between them and their patients? Why would they allow middlemen to erect so many negative barriers between them and their patients? Insurance middlemen added little if any value while dramatically increasing the cost of care to the patient.

Dr. Gross realized that to help this small business and their 10 employees receive the best care at the most reasonable cost, he not only needed to help them with access to a doctor but he also needed to find a way to help them obtain direct access to appropriately priced labs, X-rays, and imaging. He began to reach out to medical colleagues in these specialties with whom he already had developed relationships and establish a way for his patients to pay the wholesale cost of those services. When he discussed this with the lab that handled the blood work for his patients, the lab told him that the most expensive part of the lab work was the human labor associated with collecting on insurance claims. If he could guarantee and provide payment, they could cut lab costs by about 95 percent!

He contacted a local radiology clinic to ask if his patients could pay cash at time of service and if the clinic could fit his patients into open slots in their schedule when their imaging equipment was not being used. This reduced the cost of a chest X-ray to $20 instead of $125 and the costs of an MRI to $200 from $2,000.

Putting all of these things together, they created a business plan that allowed for a monthly membership price for the employer and his staff. Simple, yes? Nothing is ever that simple in the medical world, where government is involved in every nook and cranny and insurance companies—along with every other middleman from private equity to pharmacy benefit managers—have also found a way to insert themselves into the process. The truth is, Dr. Gross's epiphany was just the starting point for a journey that has now involved 10 years, enormous sums of money spent on legal and regulatory issues, and innumerable trips to Washington, D.C., to testify before Congress. But what began by accident has turned into a powerful movement. This was not a movement started by Dr. Gross alone but really by various movements started by physicians across the country who refused to take no for an answer. Now, with thousands of medical practices exploding onto the national scene, there is state-level protection for DPC practices in about 30 of the 50 states so that these practices don't have to constantly battle regulators claiming such practices are illegal insurance schemes or insurance companies or trying to find other ways to close down these medical practices.

More important than the regulatory victories won by the DPC movement are the hundreds of thousands of patients who are now receiving quality care at a much more affordable price. Most DPC practices charge around $75 per month for the first member, and less for other family members who are also a part of the program. DPC doctors are usually available to their patients around the clock. Convenience is a part of the deal. Whether the connection is by telephone, videoconference, or text, or face-to-face at the medical practice, the close relationship between the doctor and the patient is the foundation of care. Modern technology combined with deep relationships leads to quality medical care.

This strengthening of the doctor–patient relationship has a profound impact on the patient's overall cost of care. When a patient has a strong relationship with a good family doctor who oversees all of their care, the patient has far less need to see a specialist or be referred for in-patient or out-patient care by other physicians. Their own family doctor, who is usually only looking after around 500–600 patients in most DPC practices, rather than the 2,500–3,500 patients typical in insurance-based practices, can take as much time with them as necessary. DPC practitioners often take 1–2 hours the first time they meet with a new patient to make sure they fully understand the needs of the new patient and their family. Subsequent office visits are likely to be anywhere from 30–45 minutes.

All this service costs less than a cup of Starbucks coffee on the way to work each morning. This is the starting place for the K.I.S.S. approach to better access, higher quality, and lower costs.

Dr. Gross and his colleagues have spent tens of thousands of dollars on legal fees, with accountants and everyone else telling them it can't be done. But their response was, "We are going to do it anyway; we will figure it out." Before long, patients were coming from all over Florida because they could afford access to quality care that had never been available to them before. Very quickly, Dr. Gross realized that their uninsured patients, the members of their DPC practice, received much better care, faced fewer obstacles, and spent far less than their insured patients. It made no sense that a patient might pay $600 per month to an insurance company for the privilege of then paying twice as much out of pocket for the same MRI as the uninsured patient in their practice. Other than for catastrophic events, medical insurance was looking superfluous. But the ACA did not provide a way for patients to just purchase insurance to deal with larger medical events.

It is no surprise, in this context, that someone like me would come up with the medical cost-sharing approach, a non-insurance solution to the challenge of handling larger medical costs. My company Sedera, described in chapter 4, was born in this context, though at the time I had not thought through how directly our work would become linked with the work of DPC physicians. Now, we are encouraging all Sedera members to link with DPC or similar practices because of the synergies of having primary care needs handled by doctors familiar with the needs and benefits of the cash-pay patient.

OTHER INNOVATIONS

All over the country, as the word has spread, others are also coming up with variations on this theme. The level of frustration for the typical family doctor working in the insurance context has risen to a point where the pressures of the work are driving physicians to conclude there must be a better way. And driven by the nature of the free market, all sorts of interesting ideas are emerging. Texas, my home base, is a center of innovation because of its business-friendly climate. But this does not mean that all is smooth sailing.

Telemedicine is another good example of a new way to provide care for patients. The development of telemedicine around the country, even here in Texas, has been challenging. This is not just because of federal regulatory interference. State-level medical associations in many states have also been instrumental in blocking the path for doctors to make their services available by phone, text, and video conference. Teladoc and other telemedicine services have had to fight many legal and regulatory battles to persuade the powers that be that telemedicine provides another legitimate way to diagnose and treat many common diseases. But any family doctor with much clinical experience knows that if you take a good history from the patient at the beginning of the doctor–patient relationship, the doctor has a more comprehensive understanding of the context of the patient's complaint. With this and the patient's common sense in providing past experience of similar conditions, you can normally provide the patient with a good pathway forward. Whether they need a prescription now, or just advice to tide them over through the night, my guess is that 90 percent of the people who used to show up in my doctor's office could have been handled by phone. Add video conferencing, and the number would have risen to 95 percent. Statistics from medical practices that have developed a substantial medical triage through their own doctor-led call centers clearly substantiate these numbers. Again, the recent pandemic has not only confirmed the reality that 95 percent of most medical care can be provided through a virtual context, but it has even erased the rather artificial barriers that stop highly qualified and licensed physicians in one state from practicing in another state. COVID-19 may have put the final nail in the coffin of government interference, at both the federal and state level, as necessity has demanded that doctors be free to practice via telemedicine.

Patients love the access that telemedicine provides. Who wants to take time off work or arrange a babysitter for the kids to wait for 45 minutes in the doctor's office if they can deal with the situation effectively with a short phone call?

Telemedicine access on its own is already helping many people who don't feel they can afford health insurance. In nine cases out of 10, it is cheaper and better for the patient to belong to a DPC or VPC (virtual primary care via telemedicine) practice and have access to a medical cost-sharing program such as Sedera than it is to pay for an expensive health insurance plan. Even for inexpensive health insurance plans, deductibles and copays make going to the doctor an expensive out-of-pocket experience.

The DPC approach is not the only innovation that is happening in this area.

Larger entities like RosenCare, which I will introduce in the next chapter, are doing a tremendous job through on-site or near-site clinics. Companies with a few hundred employees and their families living in a relatively small geographic location, that use a self-insure model, are finding that they can dramatically cut costs by funding their own clinics for their staff and families.

In Austin, Texas, Dr. Jeremy Gabrysch has pioneered a similar approach to near-site clinics. As an ER board-certified physician, he was well aware of the fact that the ER has unfortunately become the "family doctor" to large numbers of people who don't have easy access to medical care. Everybody knows that most of the illness that presents in the ER does not need the high tech and high cost that emergency rooms are designed for.

It was the night before Thanksgiving when a friend called me about 8 p.m., very concerned about his wife. She had been experiencing dizziness, with occasional headaches, for about a month. They had finally seen a doctor a few days previously, and the doctor was working with them on some tests to try to run down what was happening. But my friend was worried that the condition was escalating. This explains the call on the night before a holiday, with the worry that finding a doctor on Thanksgiving Day might be impossible. Should they go to the emergency room?

A quick history, with a few more questions to uncover any other symptoms or signs, led me to reassure him that things would probably be fine. If he wanted to see a doctor, I gave him the number for Dr. Gabrysch's Remedy Urgent Care. If he needed to, my friend could easily go to one of their facilities, or even ask for a house call from Remedy, for a fraction of what the emergency room would cost. Reassured, and knowing that he had easy access to a doctor, he and his wife decided to wait.

As is so often the case, what the patient really wanted was access. Access to speak to a physician is frequently better than any medication. That was certainly the case here. Imagine what unnecessary tests and how much anxiety would have been caused if someone with my friend's wife's history turned up in an emergency room at 9 p.m. And that doesn't include what would probably have been $3,000 of imaging and lab work that would also have been performed. Now if the doctor thinks they are needed, any necessary imaging or labs can occur at the regularly scheduled appointment at about one-fifth of the cost.

Add in the basic costs for just turning up at an ER, and my friends probably saved $5,000 by not needing to go at all. Five thousand dollars out of pocket is much more than the cost of DPC access for a whole family for a year—a lot to waste by not knowing the system or by not understanding the value of belonging to a local DPC practice. Having a family doctor who you know, who knows you, and who is available when you need access is not an expensive choice; rather, it is the only choice that makes sense to keep your overall medical costs down.

Urgent care centers provide access to a medical provider who is well-versed in ways to intervene in the crises that take so many unnecessarily to nearby ERs. Consumers need to be educated in such a way that they understand how to get the best out of their healthcare choices. By establishing a quality relationship with a primary care physician who is readily available, most people are already well on their way to dramatically cutting their overall health costs.

Remedy Urgent Care, like a growing number of the models from doctors like Jeremy Gabrysch, is another tool that is helping to change the medical landscape for the better. The unifying thread with so many of these modern approaches to more effective, more accessible, and higher quality care at lower prices is the absence of medical insurance as the middleman. What, if anything, does a health insurance program offer in the examples that I am providing? Nothing, except high premium costs for the dubious privilege of paying more out of pocket for the care that most of us need. Removing the middleman, the hospital, the insurance company, and the pharmacy benefit manager, and reestablishing the doctor–patient relationship is at the heart of both easy access and great care.

Next Level Urgent Care in Houston and its surrounding areas is another beautiful example of what can be done with creative thinking that is not dependent on the insurance model. Dr. Juliet Breeze is another entrepreneur/physician who is changing access to healthcare. Uninsured and underinsured patients are welcomed, and these patients find that transparent pricing is typically only $175–$250 per visit. If these visits were handled through an emergency room, they would cost $1,500 to $2,000. This is a savings of 75–90 percent in most cases. On top of this, if your visit to Next Level Urgent Care requires you to be transferred to an ER because of the life-threatening nature of your condition, your care at Next Level is free.

Another innovative development at Next Level Urgent Care is the bundled pricing that includes everything connected with an episode of care. If you arrive at the clinic with an injured hand, Next Level will not bill you separately for the examination of the hand, the X-ray, and the stitches or cast. By bundling all charges into one episode of care, they provide really high value at low cost. Try comparing that to a visit to a hospital ER.

My wife, Felicity, recently had just such an experience. We were playing frisbee with our children and grandchildren. Jumping for a high catch, she came down on a rock and then fell onto her outstretched hand. We all heard the crack! I may be an experienced physician, but there is something unnerving when the patient is your wife of 48 years. We went straight to a nearby urgent care facility that operates on the principles I have described above. The initial examination, the X-rays confirming the diagnosis and nature of the break, the painkillers, the anesthetic, and the resetting of the bone by the doctor on duty came to $750, which we happily paid in full, knowing that Sedera would handle any costs above our initial unshareable amount, which for me was $500. Time in the urgent care: 90 minutes, start to finish.

If we had gone to the ER under the same circumstances, here is an estimate of what we would have ended up paying for:

1. Facility charge, just for entering the ER–$650 at the nearby hospital

2. Painkillers provided in the ER–$100

3. Physician charge for the independent, out-of-network doctor who staffs the ER–$750

4. X-ray charges for X-ray and technician–$300

5. Reading of the X-ray by outside radiologist, not on hospital payroll–$300

6. Anesthetic for resetting of the bone by anesthetist–$500, as the anesthetist operates independently of the ER staff as part of a nationwide private equity-owned anesthetic group

7. Reset of the fracture by ER hospitalist[1]–$300

Total estimated bill for the complete ER visit: $2,900. (My guess is that this is an underestimate!) Estimated time in ER: 4–6 hours.

This is the impact of the marketplace on medical competition. Pricing transparency is a powerful tool. Whether it is a company wanting to offer quality care to their employees and their families or a gig economy worker who is wondering how to handle medical costs, the starting place for quality care lies at the intersection between doctor and patient at the primary care level. Doctors and patients who understand this become willing partners in the dramatic cost savings that are the result of letting the doctor who understands the medical cash-pay ecosystem be the quarterback for the patient looking for help navigating this system. If you know your doctor, and your doctor knows you, entering the medical system for an episode of care is not frightening but reassuring. Costs are manageable without insurance artificially inflating the price. Add to this mix the patient's participation in a medical cost-sharing community for high-end expenses, and you have peace of mind about all of your medical costs. Now you are a health savvy consumer—and likely putting an extra $5,000–10,000 a year into your household budget for other things, like a great family vacation.

We have not yet even looked at the impact of these cash-friendly primary care approaches on other parts of the healthcare world such as drug costs. In many parts of the country, your primary care physician can not only prescribe drugs but also dispense those drugs to you. Whether or not this is allowed in your state, just having a physician who is aware of the cost of drugs and the dramatic savings involved in using generics in most situations has a profound impact on pharmaceutical costs. Exploring pharmacy costs, which represent about 25 percent of overall medical costs, is another vital part of the puzzle. For now, it is enough to recognize that even here it is the doctor–patient relationship that makes the most difference to these costs. When doctors care for their patients like family members, they care about how much drugs cost their patients. Relationships are key to the thinking that goes into saving you money while ensuring the highest quality in every part of your medical experience.

CHAPTER 7

OUT OF THE BOX!

HARRIS ROSEN TELLS A REMARKABLE STORY that I first heard at a Docs4PatientCare Foundation conference at a Rosen Resort in Orlando. This remarkable man, the founder, COO, and president of the hotel chain he established in 1971, was describing the health plan he had put in place over the past three decades for his now more than 6,000 employees. Here was a person who, by his own admission, knew nothing about healthcare. But he was not willing to put up with the annual increase in the cost of care for his employees, particularly because he knew that the insurance itself was covering less and less. On top of this, having made sure that his employees had easy access to care, the amount of illness among his employees had declined. So, why the constant increase in cost of premiums?

As Harris probed this question with the insurance companies, he began to learn some interesting things. One of the first was the question of "what is a group?" He had assumed that his group was limited to his own employees. But that was not the case. The insurance company put him in a group with other medium-sized employers. In spite of all of the money he was making available to give his employees access to company-sponsored clinics, access to mental health treatments, and encouragement for gym memberships and smoking cessation programs, there was no "credit" for the fact that his employees were much healthier than average employees in his industry. What could be done in this situation? What could any employer do if the insurance company was not willing to work with it outside of this "group" context or consider premium reductions on the basis of the excellent health of its workforce?

Well, he could fire his insurance company. And that is exactly what Harris Rosen did. He didn't fire them in the sense of saying, "I am going to switch from Blue Cross to Humana or change from United to Aetna." He fired the whole insurance system and decided that he was going to provide better access and better quality to his own staff directly. He suspected he could do this at considerably lower costs than he was currently experiencing by relying on insurance.

His first step was to establish a clinic with really easy access for his employees. Actually, Rosen prefers the word "associates" because that more accurately reflects the family relationship he encourages within his companies. The clinic was not just for staff but for their immediate family members as well; it was available to everyone who was previously covered under Rosen's insurance program. There was no co-pay or other out-of-pocket cost for employees or their families to see the doctor at the clinic. They were welcome to go to the clinic on company time, and if they needed transportation to get there, the company would provide it. Rosen staffed the clinic with highly experienced doctors and nurses who really cared for the associates. The clinic directly handled necessary medication, X-rays, and labs without any additional cost to the patient. If a clinic member needed to be referred to a specialist or admitted to a hospital, the clinic would pre-negotiate a price directly with that provider. Costs would be handled by the Rosen Hotel Group's internal self-insurance program.

The resort staff loved this approach. Typically, the hotel and resort industry experienced high employee turnover, and employees were less healthy than the national average. But with open access to a nearby clinic, and local clinicians navigating the patients to appropriate places to have more complex—and therefore more expensive—tests and labs that could not be done on site, prices plummeted.

Quickly it became clear that overall costs were not only being contained, but that the health of the team was improving. Easy access to healthcare was stabilizing treatment for diabetics and reducing visits to emergency rooms. This model honestly faced obesity as a health issue. Smoking challenges could be addressed head on, with the clinic offering the help needed to quit. Drug abuse and other inappropriate ways to handle the ordinary pressures of life for company associates could be addressed in compassionate and effective ways.

I found this success story so fascinating that I arranged to meet and interview Harris Rosen and his team, and they graciously agreed. When asked whether he had felt qualified to make these changes in the health program for his team, Rosen's response showed both his humility and the true heart of this entrepreneur:

> Healthcare is not a subject that many of us know much, if anything, about. But I was stupid enough to believe that we could learn. We were growing, and we were moving our accounting office out of a little free-standing building. We were contemplating converting that into some sort of a daycare facility. My

idea was to use that little building and create our own little medical center, a primary care facility. When I shared that idea with others, they looked at me like I'd lost my mind. But I proceeded, and we found a wonderful primary care doctor. We were ready to operate, much to our surprise.

Our little clinic did beautifully. However, we had to negotiate with hospitals and other physicians. Then we had complete coverage for all of our associates. We put the little package together. We said a prayer and we were off and running, much to our surprise!

We reduced our cost per covered life dramatically, and it was such an extraordinary reduction that people were talking about it. One of the large magazines here in Florida, *The Florida Trend*, heard about what we had done. They interviewed me because they were so taken by what we had accomplished. They put us on the cover of the magazine, and that's how it all began. It is not something that I would recommend others do, because it was probably a bit insane. But I have done things like that in the past, and I suspect I'll do things like that in the future.

This is the language of the entrepreneur, of the change agent. When CEOs around the country start sounding like Harris Rosen and sharing in his passion to take care of his employees, they will find the courage to bring similar changes into their own situation. As someone once put it, "When we are willing to do what others are unwilling to do, we will be able to accomplish what others are unable to accomplish." Mr. Rosen continued:

Today, with about 6,000 covered lives, including dependents, our cost per covered life has, of course, increased dramatically since those early days 30 years ago. But still, we discover that we are about half of what the cost per covered life is nationwide here in America. Sadly, it doesn't look like we've completed the task, even though we've had dramatic success. We have a long way to go. Our hope and our prayer is that others in the private sector will join us in the years to come.

Those remarks match my own hope in the writing of this book. When those of us who have control of our own companies' healthcare spending take our courage in our hands and demand radical change, and not just marginal improvements to the company healthcare coverage, change will come. Let me illustrate with a situation that we had in one of the companies that I started.

My first company, The Karis Group, had grown over the years and was providing medical cost containment to companies all over the United States. But we were struggling with our own employee healthcare costs. I had already started Sedera, which by then was providing an alternative to the insurance model to 100 other companies across the country. But the administrative staff at my first company was suspicious of this new sharing model. Would it really be able to handle the costs of major medical incidents for our staff if and when such incidents occurred? What about this newfangled idea I was talking about of paying all our staff a stipend to have access to local direct primary care doctors? Was I going to force employees to let go of the family doctors they had known over many years, even though they could never get in to see those doctors when the need was urgent? And this idea of using telemedicine after hours . . . could a doctor really help you without seeing you, just by a consultation over the phone? Anyway, my senior staff would never agree to a non-insurance solution, or so I was told.

Finally, in exasperation, I told the benefits team that they had no choice. If we had been able to help so many people in our previous 20 years of experience in medical cost containment, and I was able to help so many in my 15 years of medical work before that, why did they doubt that our own team would benefit from the same methodology? "From here on out," I told the team, "we will only pay a defined contribution towards medical costs." This would easily cover the cost of the Sedera and DPC approach, but it would barely cover half of the cost of the insurance plans that people "loved" so much, even though those same plans did not deliver half what people hoped they would.

Despite a certain amount of grumbling to my face and behind my back, we went forward with this approach. Within a year, virtually everyone had not only dropped their objections, but had fallen in love with the impact of DPC and the Sedera model on their health and on their finances.

Any CEO with the courage to grow in this area will find many insights in the lessons from Harris Rosen's journey of helping his employees toward lower costs and higher quality care. Let me share a few more nuggets that he and his team shared with me:

There are a couple of different models as it relates to Rosen-Care.[1] Our model for our hotel employees is a mandatory program. If you work at Rosen and you want healthcare, you do have to use our model. We have another large employer, the school board of Osceola County, that uses a voluntary approach. And we have incentives and steerage to help move employees and their family members in the direction that will provide the highest quality care at the best possible price. But as these things apply to Rosen employees and incentives, there is a culture here starting at the very top.

Our incentives are why our costs from premiums are strangely low for the employee and their family members. There are hardly any out-of-pocket expenses. We do not have deductibles. We do not have co-insurance. Ninety percent of our drugs are free. We also have a lot of communication about wellness. We have wellness programs such as Zumba, tai chi and bootcamps. All these physical fitness and wellness initiatives, things like Weight Watchers, don't cost anything to the employee. I think the employees' value that greatly, and it causes them to move in the direction of wanting to be healthier individuals.

What does this do for us? It saves us a lot of money, but also our employee turnover is probably the lowest in the hospitality industry. Restaurants and hotel turnover ranges from 50–80 percent per year. We turn over a little bit more than 10 percent. And most of that is people retiring. We have many people in their 70s and 80s working for us. Keep the costs down. Keep it simple. Everyone benefits from that.

With this flow of wisdom from Harris Rosen and his senior team, I couldn't help but ask, "What do you have to say to the CEOs or CFOs who are beginning to say 'We've got to do something to change our situation. How do we take seriously our responsibility as a business in dealing with this area?'" Mr. Rosen's answer is clear:

After employee wages, healthcare is probably the next largest line item on the profit and loss statement. So, it's interesting that you mentioned the CEO and the CFO, because it is, in our opinion, absolutely critical to have those individuals engaged. Part of the reason we're in the situation that we are in now with healthcare is because most CEOs and CFOs say, "Hey, I'm handling our core business. We've got a lot of stuff going on. I'm going to let someone else handle that."

In order to change healthcare around the country, it certainly won't happen at the rapid speed that it needs to happen without the CEO and CFO absolutely engaged. We tell them, "Yeah, you might run a hotel, you might run a widget factory. But guess what? You also run a healthcare company." CEOs and CFOs can improve. The question is, do they have an incentive to do it? Do they have the courage to do it? More and more chief executives will ask themselves, "Why can't we do that, too?" And that's what I'm hoping for in time.

Our conversation was filled with so much wisdom that the only way I could communicate it accurately was to quote what he told me. But, as is often the case, he saved the best for last. As we were wrapping up, one member of the team mentioned that over the past 30 years, they have saved approximately $400 million. Wow! That is a huge amount of money to put toward the bottom line of any company. But typical of how Mr. Rosen thinks, when you dig into the impact of these savings, they have led not just to better pay and benefits for his associates, but these savings have also been the engine for a massive amount of philanthropy poured into local needy communities. The impact on the Tangelo Park area of Orlando has been so noticeable that *The New York Times* published an article on the amazing, transformational work done through Harris Rosen's generosity.[2]

Businesses have a growing number of good options for dealing with employee healthcare costs. The key issue in planning for this is to make sure that all employees and their families have easy access to primary care, which can be handled very effectively via virtual primary care at a reasonable cost. This has such an impact on both quality of care and access to care when it is paired with the Sedera medical cost-sharing approach. Sedera is able to reduce the medical cost-sharing monthly fee because members taken care of by quality virtual primary care end up costing the sharing community less money in hospitalizations and other high-cost medical procedures.

For both the employer and the employee, there are some key issues that need to be addressed. Employees want and need medical insurance or the medical cost-sharing model to be able to travel with them from job to job. Having healthcare tied to a job is counterproductive when you want to move to a new location or a new work environment. Recent executive orders creating the Individual Choice Health Reimbursement Arrangement, or ICHRA, have greatly simplified this process. The ICHRA essentially allows the employer to get out of the healthcare business by making it simple to put quality choices in front of the employee for them to *choose* what is best for them and their family. The employer still engages with some of the costs, at the level they determine the company can afford, but the employee is then allowed to deploy the money. Everybody is the winner in this scenario. Just make sure that you have the right people advising you. Currently few brokers really understand the role of the ICHRA in freeing up employers to move out of the healthcare business while still being able to provide financially for benefits as a part of the whole salary package that employees are looking for.

Some similar sentiments are very clearly articulated by another very famous physician, Dr. Atul Gawande, the former CEO of Haven (the Berkshire Hathaway/Amazon/J.P. Morgan Chase joint venture). Dr. Gawande's books such as *The Checklist Manifesto* and *Complications* have had a huge impact across the country. In a conversation with Dr. Robert Wachter, chair of the University of California, San Francisco,

Department of Medicine, that appeared in Becker's Hospital Review, Dr. Gawande had this to say:

> "America's healthcare . . . system is [a] flawed . . . employer-based system. A job-based system is a broken system in a world where people are moving every couple of years . . . [T]ying your healthcare to your job, that remains . . . a big hill to climb, and the government has to solve it."[3]

For large employers with the vision and courage of a Harris Rosen, on-site clinics and self-insure plans can be an awesome way to go. But for most CEOs of small to medium sized companies, who feel they already have too much to focus on to tackle such a large area, recent changes, such as the ICHRA, allow them to move toward a defined contribution model that essentially takes them and their companies out of the insurance business. Instead, decisions on healthcare can be put into the employees' hands, along with the education and advice that will allow the type of cash-based models that I have been describing in this book to work incredibly well for their employees. Thousands of companies nationwide are already moving into these models involving DPC and Sedera medical cost-sharing and seeing huge savings along with much greater employee engagement because of the higher quality care.

OTHER PHYSICIANS MAKING THE LEAP

The most amazing people are turning to this approach. Dr. Firouz Daneshgari is a world-class surgeon. Credited by many as the father of the urological sub-specialty known as female urological reconstructive surgery, a number of years ago he took the unprecedented step of resigning his professorial chair at a university. Why would a surgeon of such renown take this step? Two vital personal principles pushed him to this decision.

First, he felt the need to make healthcare more accessible to all. As a physician, he had pledged his life and his skills to "First do no harm." How could he reconcile this with the growing understanding that so many of his patients were being permanently damaged by the financial component of needing surgery, even when they had insurance? In fact, according to the Kaiser Family Foundation,[4] 62 percent of people who have problems paying their medical bills have health insurance.

Dr. Daneshgari was also beginning to think through how to effect significant change within the medical profession. He had become aware of the direct primary care practices that were transforming primary care, and his academic background convinced him that this movement had the potential to radically reduce medical costs. He knew that by removing the middlemen from medicine and returning the doctor to the primary place of influence, doctors steer patients transparently, with an appreciation for the financial impact that further treatment has on the patient. By moving to direct primary care, Dr. Daneshgari's experience has become another driver to improve the system of care available to patients.

Dr. Daneshgari's DPC practice, BowTie Medical, had a most interesting early client. This group of 2,000 people came to BowTie to help them run their emerging medical cost-sharing community. Rather than using an insurance model, these families had come together without contract or compulsion, voluntarily agreeing to share each other's medical bills on an organized basis. BowTie was contracted to provide the medical care and administer their program. As an academic, a long-term researcher, and an innovator, Dr. Daneshgari understood the importance of tracking both cost and quality of medical care in this interesting population of people joined by their common faith and commitment to make the sharing approach work.

Over the first 18 months of helping this fledgling medical cost-sharing community, Dr. Daneshgari learned many interesting things.

Although this community was only charging its members around one third of the typical insurance cost for people of this age and geographic distribution, the community was still accumulating money at an almost unbelievable rate. In the first year and a half, the community received $939,307 to share toward medical bills from its members, but only needed $111,153 to handle the cost of the medical bills. In insurance language, this would be a medical loss ratio of approximately 11.8%. This is just fancy language for saying they only needed 11.8% of the money they had collected to handle all of the community's medical bills for those 18 months. The community could then look to see if it needed to adjust its rates further downward.

If these stories do nothing more than give us hope, we have made a start. But what RosenCare and BowTie Medical have done is just scratching the surface. Amazing things are already happening within innovative health plans and medical practices across the country. From presidential executive orders mandating hospital pricing transparency to the rapid expansion of groups such as the Free Market Medical Association, change is happening.

Now, begin to think about these kinds of cost reductions spreading on a national scale. Historically, Americans have expected and relied on annual salary increases that a company may provide to keep up with cost-of-living expenses. Due to healthcare cost inflation, a generation of working people have little expectation of an increase in their standard of living year by year. The past 30 years of forced annual health insurance premium increases have effectively robbed most people with ordinary incomes of the salary raises they might typically expect, even as the insurance they were paying for has provided fewer benefits each year.

By applying the lessons learned from the stories of the pioneers in this book, every company could be back on the road to prosperity. Rather than living with the lack of choices and high costs of government-sponsored plans under the ACA, gig economy workers can become savvy healthcare consumers. Private individuals and families can be a part of this revolution. Anyone who makes decisions on healthcare costs and healthcare choices needs to become a savvy consumer.

CHAPTER 8

POLICY MATTERS

L EO TOLSTOY WROTE, "IN OUR WORLD everybody thinks of changing humanity, and nobody thinks of changing himself."[1] What indeed is the role of personal responsibility in transforming our healthcare system in the United States to create lower costs, better access and higher quality? What policies and regulations should we create or jettison to support needed changes? As you can imagine, many smart people have given this subject a lot of thought. In the face of substantial challenges to fixing our healthcare system, like pre-existing conditions, chronic illness, and poverty, these innovators have developed amazing solutions.

DR. GRAY AND PERSONALIZED HEALTHCARE

A good example is in Hickory, North Carolina. Dr. Clare Gray is an experienced internist affiliated with the Catawba Valley Medical Center in Hickory. When I last spoke with him, he had just completed eight consecutive months of practice (yes, that's around 240 days, with only 14 not on call) because of the COVID-19 crisis. And in his "spare time" he was tirelessly helping to shape the medical policy future for the United States. Physicians for Reform, the organization that he helped to form, has been at the forefront of medical policy discussions for more than a decade. Dr. Gray's book, *The Battle for America's Soul: Healthcare, the Culture War, and the Future of Freedom*, provides a rallying cry for action at this time of profound change in America. As Dr. Gray eloquently describes in his book, "For perhaps the first time in American history, *We, The People*, fear our government. Not in a partisan sense, but in the sense that Washington seems deaf to the ordinary citizen, in the sense that politicians have squandered our children's future for the sake of political gain, in the sense that 'greater good' now consumes individual liberty."[2]

In the American healthcare debate, there have been two primary approaches to policy issues. The approach of the Affordable Care Act is to let government try to sort out every detail, every issue large or small, on behalf of the people. Two thousand plus pages of the law, along with another 20,000 plus pages of regulations to interpret the law, leaves all of us reeling. How can anyone understand the weight of this burden? The intention is good, but the outcome is oppressive. How do "We, the People" find our way through this mess? Dr. Gray has helped shape a simple platform that I have borrowed from to form the three guide rails that we return to again and again in this book: lower costs, better access, and higher quality.

Physicians for Reform has amplified this in a statement of less than 500 words. I have copied this, with permission, below:[3]

Your Health. Your Doctor. Your Wallet. Your Choice.

Who do you want to make your personal, private, and sometimes difficult medical decisions? You and your doctor? Or a bureaucrat in Washington?

Remember, whoever pays holds the power to choose.

Personalized Healthcare puts you and your doctor back at the center of American healthcare.

1: You control your own healthcare dollar.
Because you own your own personalized plan, you are in control. You can use your plan for yourself & your loved ones, and/or pass it on to your children with your estate.

2: Because you own your own health insurance policy, it goes with you if you change or lose your job.
Employers do not pay corporate tax on money spent providing health insurance for their employees, and employees do not pay personal income tax on their health benefits. However, individuals purchasing individual insurance do not enjoy these tax breaks. This explains why the vast majority of Americans receive their health insurance through the workplace. This limits consumer choice.

By leveling the playing field, individuals would be free to purchase insurance [or a medical cost-sharing program] with the same advantages as those who get their health insurance through the workplace.

3: You are protected if you have a pre-existing condition.

Guaranteed Coverage Pools in each state give you, and every American, the assurance that even if you have a pre-existing condition, you have access to affordable health insurance.

4: The cost of your prescription drugs will come down.

The skyrocketing cost of medicines is fueled by unnecessary middlemen and profiteers who will no longer stand between you & the medicine you need.

5: Rein in the runaway cost of insurance.

In every industry, transparency, choice & competition lowers prices & drives innovation. Because you control your healthcare dollars, insurance companies will compete for your business with insurance plans that provide what you need at prices you can afford. No more paying for expensive "one size fits all" insurance.

6: Remove bureaucratic roadblocks that interfere with your care when you are sick.

Red tape and regulations eat up over half of your doctors' time, limiting the time they can spend with you. Eliminating needless bureaucracy & regulations lets your doctor focus on what they really care about—you!

7: See the doctors you want to see hen you need to see them.

When you control your healthcare dollar you get to see the doctor you need and choose. Without middlemen and bureaucrats standing between you and your doctor, you will be amazed at how affordable routine medical care really is.

8: Reduce your cost of healthcare by protecting doctors from frivolous lawsuits.

Physicians often order every conceivable test simply to protect themselves against a possible frivolous and expensive lawsuit. This increases the cost of medical care by endless billions.

I do not believe Dr. Gray's outline is perfect, but I admire it because it is simple. Any of us can understand this. Congress could pass a law this simple if it chooses. Instead of bureaucrats trying to order every detail of this most private part of our lives, we could again become the mature and responsible adults that most of us desire to be.

But laws this simple only work when we are ready to take on personal responsibility. We must not look for someone else to make every decision for us, but rather we must exercise our own choices through our own free will by taking responsibility for ourselves. This is not an impossible dream but a reality that is already happening in various contexts where people are given the opportunity to take personal responsibility.

CHALLENGING ISSUES

But what happens in the challenging areas where public policy is needed to deal with intractable problems like pre-existing conditions, chronic illness, and the poor?

Pre-existing Conditions, Medical Cost-Sharing, and Personal Responsibility

Healthcare is not a right. This is not because we don't all need it, but precisely because we do all need it and someone has to pay for it. When my "right" to healthcare only comes because you are forced to pay for it, then it is not actually a "right" but rather an abdication of my personal responsibility. When I make the choice to be responsible for my own health, by healthy living, and for my own healthcare, by finding a way to handle my own medical bills, then I am living responsibly. When I make these choices in association with others who are willing to assume the same personal responsibility, then I am moving toward community.

It is totally appropriate for us to make plans to handle the unplanned major medical bills that could hit any of us at any time. This is a great reason to be part of a medical cost-sharing community. It is completely inappropriate to join a medical cost-sharing community precisely because you know you are going to need expensive care and you want others to pay for that care. Any community founded on members deliberately taking advantage of each other will rapidly fall apart. Liberty is the ability to live responsibly in an environment where you know others will carry the same responsibility. This is the essence of a thriving community.

So how does a just society deal with people who have expensive medical needs but have not prepared for them? When someone has an expensive pre-existing condition that they need to deal with, how should those costs be shared? Should those costs be shared in a medical cost-sharing community?

It is important to acknowledge that we need to find answers to these questions that don't abandon the needy among us. Although the issue of pre-existing conditions has become synonymous with the Affordable Care Act, the ACA did not invent this issue. Before the ACA was passed in 2010, nearly every state already had a way of helping people who were in this position. Most states used what was known as a high-risk pool.

If you had a pre-existing condition and didn't have any medical insurance, you had an extremely high risk—actually a 100-percent likelihood—of having medical bills that you didn't know how to pay for. States like Texas, where I live, had a high-risk pool available for anyone who found themselves in this position. Insurance companies were asked to administer the funds in the high-risk pool and to demonstrate that the funds were spent wisely. If there was any shortfall in the funds in the risk pool, then the state would make up that loss out of taxpayer money. The sick person with the pre-existing condition was responsible for paying twice the normal cost of health insurance because they had either chosen to go without insurance while well or had possibly allowed their insurance to lapse if laid off from work rather than using COBRA, which is prohibitively expensive for people at the lower end of the economic spectrum. If the insurance company could not cover the costs of the pre-existing conditions in this high-risk pool for the double premium they were receiving from those people, they could then go to the state to request the balance from tax dollars.

This was not a perfect system, but the model recognized the necessity of both personal responsibility and societal responsibility to ensure a minimum standard of care for all in society. Typically, people were only eligible for the high-risk pool if they had already been turned down by a recognized insurance company.

This very brief discussion of pre-existing conditions and how they were handled prior to the ACA is not designed to provide detailed answers. Rather, it helps us all to realize that you cannot magically conjure up answers to intractable problems, and you cannot ignore those problems. They need to be faced head on. Detailed study, such as that done by the Kaiser Family Foundation, helps us understand the scope of these issues and explores various ways to handle them for the two percent or so of the population that consistently fall into this category.[4]

I want to make clear that medical cost-sharing communities are not a good fit for some people with pre-existing conditions, and people with pre-existing conditions need different options. It does not make sense to conflate this serious problem with the entirely rational and economically sound tools provided through the medical cost-sharing world to the 98 percent of the population who are willing and able to take responsibility for themselves. Health insurance could and should be a different, responsible approach, but it has become corrupted by greed and government interference to such an extent that it needs to be replaced, not reformed.

The medical cost-sharing approach is designed for those who understand that any desire to offset known medical costs for which we are personally responsible onto other people cannot be sustained in any mature and stable community. Precisely because there is no transfer of risk from the individual to the wider community, medical cost-sharing will only work when responsible people choose to be associated in community with other responsible people. Each of us bears personal responsibility alongside many other people who are also willing to share in this personally responsible approach. If people are not willing to carry their own risk and be responsible for themselves, they need to use a guaranteed approach, such as insurance. For an agreed, contractual price, they can shift their unknown risks to a pool of others doing the same thing. Don't be surprised to learn this insurance approach will cost you much more!

Chronic Illness

The same issues that we have discussed in relation to pre-existing conditions apply equally to the modern Western challenges of chronic illness. An estimated 70 to 80 percent of healthcare costs are tied up with lifestyle-related chronic illnesses. Let me phrase that differently. Seventy to 80 percent of our society's healthcare costs are self-induced through our lifestyle choices. This has both profound philosophical and economic consequences for all of us. The first thing to say is that any patient with a chronic condition will find that membership in a DPC provides an amazing return on investment. Direct primary care practices are both financially and medically ideal to handle chronic illness. The doctor–patient relationship can provide the education and consistent care that are the foundation of dealing with chronic illness.

But there are other issues that get to the heart of the economic questions forced on us by people's lifestyle choices. Let me illustrate. In my company, let's say that there are two 25-year-old men who started working for us at the same time. In our company plan, both men pay the same amount for access to the medical cost-sharing community. One has been a smoker for years, does not like exercise, and is approximately 75 pounds overweight. The other is a fitness fanatic, eats well, and seems to be at an ideal weight. Statistically, over their approximately 40-year career, the medical expenses of one will be around six times as much as the other. How should the community handle this challenge? Can a medical cost-sharing community accommodate people whose lifestyle choices lead to chronic illness? How do you deal with chronic conditions that have nothing to do with lifestyle choices but are the result of genetic predisposition or other uncontrollable factors such as those that occur in type 1 diabetes or multiple sclerosis?

Many illnesses for which there currently are no cures will lead to chronic conditions that also need to be considered. Some, such as serious genetic conditions, fall into the category of extremely expensive and rare conditions for which medical science is moving toward solutions, but those solutions may be prohibitively expensive. Are these situations where the risk pool concept provides a way for society to share together in the cost? These conditions are outliers that need to be deliberately and thoughtfully planned for without damaging the rational economic principles upon which the care of the 98 percent should be based.

Similarly, there are effective ways to help anyone dealing with a very common chronic condition, such as asthma or type 1 diabetes, without breaking the bank but without taking away personal responsibility. I have a granddaughter who became a type 1 diabetic at the age of nine. No one chooses to have type 1 diabetes. Medical care continues to dramatically improve, and technology is now virtually at a place where it can provide an artificial pancreas administering insulin to the patient continuously, as needed. Yes, this is costly, but this is not outside the capacity of either insurance or a medical cost-sharing community to handle. There are no perfect economic answers, but there are compassionate choices that we make within the medical cost-sharing world. In our case, we progressively take on any new member's existing chronic conditions over a period of time. In the first year, a new member will carry the full responsibility for the cost of their condition themselves. This helps all realize that personal responsibility for a pre-existing condition does not automatically fall to other people; the chronically ill member carries responsibility as well. But we will share within the community a growing portion of the cost of that condition over time. In the example of type 1 diabetes, additional costs to a family are likely to be around $10,000–20,000 per year for the quality treatment and control that is already available. In the Sedera cost-sharing model, health consequences after the first year, such as hospitalization for out-of-control sugar levels, would be shared, but the chronic treatment cost of insulin would not. Again, this is not a perfect solution, but it does recognize that complicated situations need rational and compassionate answers. Our answer is a good step in that direction while still recognizing that our healthcare is our own responsibility. We are continuing to explore how a community of people can willingly and voluntarily share in the challenging situations of some members suffering from chronic illness.

The answers here are neither simple nor found in ever more powerful pills and potions. I believe medical cost-sharing communities can take on members who have made poor lifestyle choices but only if the unhealthy member will make lifestyle changes to become healthy. John Oberg, a long-standing personal friend and my Sedera co-founder, has become an expert in this area. Let me quote him from a conversation we recently had.

> The rapid growth of chronic disease around the world that I am focused on are the classic illnesses of the West. This is not to say that we should look away from problems caused by infectious diseases such as malaria or intestinal worms or tuberculosis. But I am studying the classically Western diseases such as diabetes and hypertension and COPD (chronic obstructive pulmonary disease) and heart failure, along with the anxiety and depression that are so prevalent in the West and growing at an alarming rate.

This turned our conversation toward the prevention and treatment of such diseases. John had a fair amount of skepticism about my rather simplistic thinking on how to help people make lifestyle choices that would allow for better health. He has a much greater understanding of the impact of behavioral health psychology on what it takes for people to actually be able to change behavior. It became clear as we talked that, for most people, it takes much more than self-discipline to change one's behavior. There are personal choices to be made, but we make those choices in an environment that is complex and ever changing. It can be difficult to eat healthier foods when one lives in a food desert or on a fixed income. It can be unsafe to exercise outside if one lives in a dangerous neighborhood. One example John gave that really caught my attention was about his friend who went into oncology because "the patients are really committed."

The fear of death is a strong motivator, moving the cancer patient toward whatever changes they need to make and whatever treatment they need to receive to survive. There is much to learn from the holistic treatment of the whole person in the cancer world and how the lessons learned can be applied to deal with chronic illness.

Typically, a cancer patient is surrounded by a team of people who are looking holistically at the patient and their condition, in many cases, by adding new resources to help solve difficult circumstances. John described to me the situation of another friend with serious cancer.

This friend, who was diagnosed with stage 2 cancer, was given all types of counseling. His kids were taken in for therapy. His wife was given supportive therapy. He was given mental health counseling. In addition to the oncology work they were doing, he was also given a two-inch notebook of how to handle all of his finances through such a challenging time. And the cancer center provided a counselor to take him through how to monitor all of these different people and how to put this network of healthcare professionals together in such a way as to deal with the needs of the whole family.

Learning how to provide a similarly supportive structure around the person dealing with chronic illness is a worthy goal. Chronic illness is hard for people to handle because the pain of change feels so immediate. Can a caring medical cost-sharing community, working closely with the member and their primary care physician, come together to provide the impetus for change that will be the hallmark of dealing with a chronic condition? The work of Dr. Doug Eby and the Alaska Native Medical Center provides an inspiring example of thinking about ways to deal with both chronic disease and the equally compelling challenge of poverty.

Poverty

Chronic conditions are, in many cases, closely tied to the socioeconomic conditions in which people live. Certain serious infectious diseases, like tuberculosis, frequently inhabit a challenging world where social conditions are exacerbated by pervasive poverty and lack of opportunity. Other issues such as lack of education, of vision, or of hope for the future also come to mind. Let's look at one amazing example of change in this area to see what we can learn. I want to describe an innovation in medical care that has been ongoing for the past 20 years in Alaska among the Native American population.

Dr. Douglas Eby of the Alaska Native Medical Center has helped to produce a remarkable model of medical care for a group that faced many roadblocks to change. In Alaska, many Native Americans have moved to urban centers such as Anchorage and become dislocated from their rural cultural roots. Joblessness and poverty are frequent consequences of such population movements. The hopelessness and despair that accompany these social conditions lead to much higher rates of depression and other mental illnesses and chronic medical conditions.

Twenty years ago, the Alaska Native Medical Center was a federally owned and run center that looked after 45,000 patients in a depressed urban area. The clinic and the population that it served fell in the bottom 20 percent of all medical metrics. But then the Native-owned Southcentral Foundation took over the hospital and clinic and brought in a team, including Dr. Eby, to completely change the culture and services provided. Twenty years later, the transformation is nothing short of remarkable.

Hearing Dr. Eby talk about these changes, you cannot help but be impressed with how such an at-risk population has been able to adapt to the benefits of moving into a patient-centered system. (Actually, people who visit the clinic are not called patients anymore. Rather, they are respectfully viewed and referred to as "customer–owners.") The customer–owner controls all of the key variables in treatment, including following medical direction, taking medication, and changing eating habits. Customer–owners measure success by what they learn to do differently. They now have the personal responsibility to change their eating habits, or stop smoking, or become more consistent in tracking their blood sugar. With all of the messiness of human relationships, Dr. Eby and the other staff members serve primarily as coaches, mentors, and friends with particular medical skills. The goal is to change behavior in ways that lead to better health.

Now, 20 years in, the clinic and its population are in the top 25 percent for all medical and mental health metrics. The "happiness factor" is dramatically up. Alcoholism and despair are dramatically down. Diabetes is well-controlled. Twenty years ago, most of the population had no personal relationship with a doctor, and even getting an appointment might have taken weeks or months. As a result, "primary care" happened primarily in emergency rooms and urgent care centers. Now, the clinic guarantees every patient same-day appointments within the primary care system. Fifty percent of interactions with the primary care physician are asynchronous, not face-to-face or by phone. Another 30 percent are synchronous but virtual. Telemedicine has proven invaluable. Only 20 percent of primary care contacts occur in person. As I heard Dr. Eby say in a podcast, "The doctor's role is to weave ourselves into the tapestry of our patients' lives."[5]

By removing the barriers to developing relationships between doctors and their patients, the clinic now provides a quality medical home to a massive population that spreads out way beyond Anchorage. The clinic's service territory now includes 50 outlying remote villages in an area so large that it would actually count as America's seventh-largest state if considered on its own. Amazingly, all of this treatment is provided at half the price of other clinics serving similar size populations elsewhere within Alaska. You really can have higher quality at half the cost if you respectfully rebuild the doctor–patient relationship.

UNDERSTANDING THE TAX IMPLICATION OF HEALTH INSURANCE

I want to end this chapter on medical policy and regulation with some simple thoughts on the impact of taxes on the medical system. There is no one solution that will solve the complexities of what is best for the country with regard to taxes. However, I can point out the natural consequences of decisions made in Washington, D.C., and help make sure we are at least thinking about long-term consequences.

Following World War II, the federal government exercised control over prices and wages. Businesses that wanted to hire and retain the best talent began offering increasingly rich benefits because tax law allowed corporations to pay employee benefits with pre-tax dollars. However, this only applied to businesses buying benefits, including health insurance, for their employees. People working for themselves or those not in a traditional employer–employee relationship (i.e., people on 1099s) were not allowed an equal tax break for money spent on medical benefits. Why this distinction? I don't know. But it clearly put those who had to pay for their own health benefits at a serious disadvantage. It also created the rather perverse "benefit" of giving the greatest tax advantage to those in the highest earning brackets. I have no problem with people earning high incomes, but why give them more advantage in buying health insurance than someone who is earning less money and is in a lower income bracket? Surely politicians of good will on both sides of the aisle could find a way to agree to bring common sense into such a situation.

Similarly, why do we only make a popular innovation like tax-deductible health savings accounts (HSAs) available to people who buy high-deductible health plans? Why not make them available to everyone, as Ben Carson recommended when he ran for president? Tax policy should encourage sensible behaviors. Putting money away toward future medical expenses is clearly a sensible thing to do. Let's reward behavior that prepares people for the challenge of future medical expenses. This also dramatically cuts the overall cost of insurance, while teaching people to take care of smaller expenses themselves rather than relying on insurance to do what they can easily plan for. It also makes sense to allow people to use HSAs for any approach to handling medical expenses, not just health insurance. People should be able to make their own choices about how they use their healthcare dollars. Medical cost-sharing programs, such as those provided by Sedera, are clearly every bit as legitimate as health insurance programs in handling medical costs and should share similar advantages under the tax code. This isn't a political issue; it is a common-sense issue. Let's help people who are helping themselves and who don't want to take from the public purse.

Dr. Elaina George, a well-known ear, nose, and throat surgeon in Atlanta, touches on these issues in her book, *Big Medicine: The Cost of Corporate Control and How Doctors and Patients Working Together Can Rebuild a Better System*. Dr. George has pioneered a direct cash model for ENT surgery that reflects her belief that fair pricing puts surgery within reach for everyone. Reflecting on the purpose of the law that made it possible for all people to be seen in emergency rooms whether or not they could afford to pay, she notes the unintended impact of government intervention: "Unfortunately, this unfunded congressional mandate led to the unintended consequence of people using the emergency medical system for primary care. Hospitals, even nonprofits, despite having access to government money set aside to pay them to cover these patients, have continued to pass along the cost of delivering 'free' healthcare to paying customers—essentially double dipping. This contributes to the explosion in the cost of hospital care."

I would add to what Dr. George has said that in the case of nonprofit hospitals, this is essentially "triple dipping," because they also reap the benefit of their tax-exempt status at the taxpayer expense. Dr. George is one of the most articulate and outspoken physicians through her popular internet radio show, "Living in the Solution with Dr. Elaina George." As she also said in her book, "One of the greatest harms we do is to remain quiet. Physicians need to explain what is happening to their patients, and together, they must make their voices heard before individual choices are legislated away."[6]

It is time to look carefully at where the rubber meets the road. How should individuals, families, and businesses of every size make these decisions? How do we answer the question, "What should I be doing about handling medical costs?" Let's dig into this question next.

CHAPTER 9

BE CAREFUL WHOSE ADVICE YOU TRUST

GIVEN THE INCREDIBLE OPPORTUNITY for quality and savings offered by the emerging free market healthcare ecosystem, how should an individual or a company best put together a plan that suits them? It is wise to have great advisors, but you need to be clear with your advisors about what you are looking for. There is an inevitable tension between our need for advice and our subsequent responsibility to choose whether to take such advice.

The partner to advice is action. You need to understand enough to form your own opinion based on expert advice. Getting advice is wise. But deciding on your own course of action is where you add your wisdom and your objectives to others' advice. This chapter is about those who advise and what action you should take in response.

To make the free-market healthcare ecosystem work for you, you must first understand the various layers of the onion that need to be discarded to get to the core of quality healthcare. By doing so, you will ensure you only consent to decisions that lead to your desired outcomes of lower costs, better access, and higher quality. For too long we have all been lulled into thinking that healthcare is too complicated for ordinary people to make the decisions. Instead, we have been led to hand this area over to a broker/advisor so that they can make the decisions for us.

This is a huge mistake.

To understand why, just ask yourself, "Who is paying the broker?" In most cases, it is the insurance company. Most people do what they are paid to do. It is hard for brokers to buck the system, though a growing number are willing to do just that. Nelson Griswold of Bottom Line Solutions, who organizes the annual Ascend Conference, is a well-recognized leader in this area. The Health Rosetta team of accredited brokers would fit into this same picture, as would many individual brokers and agents around the country. Just as more and more doctors have chosen to take the risk of charting their own path in the direct primary care world, a growing group of brokers is waking up to the fact that the only way to offer quality, unbiased advice to a client is to be paid by the client rather than the insurance company. The financial planning world went in this direction years ago when their early pioneers became "fee only" financial planners. These financial planners were being paid for their advice rather than taking income from the sale of insurance products. In the health world, this innovation would be a great first step to making sure you are getting unbiased advice. Ask your broker to drop any commissions. Where possible, have those commissions removed from any monthly premiums or sharing costs that you are handling and then pay the broker a generous fee based on how much they are saving you and your company.

Whether we are talking about an individual family budget or the corporate bottom line, healthcare expenses must be a high priority if we are going to protect our finances. At the family level, annual increases in insurance premiums have effectively negated most annual pay increases. Even worse, the medical system gone mad creates the constant threat of personal bankruptcy when unexpected health expenses occur. Instead of being able to save, we have had to pay more each year in premiums. Instead of better benefits at less cost, we have increasingly limited benefits at ever higher costs. We all need to stand up and take responsibility for reversing this trend and putting our families, our businesses, and our country on a track that again believes abundance is normal and that the next generation can prosper as much as or even more than the previous generation. Where are the advisors with this attitude and the track record to prove it?

Personal experience is often the best instructor. Let me start with some stories from my own experience along this journey.

MY CEO'S EXPERIENCE WITH HEALTH INSURANCE VS. SEDERA

Jamie Lagarde was the first employee that I brought on back in 2014, when Sedera was just an idea. A close friend and board member of my first company, the Karis Group (now Point Health), introduced us. Jamie caught the vision that I cast to such an extent that he chose to wind down his own company so that he could join me in what he described as a "bigger idea." He told me that in discussing this with his wife, he said, "I prefer Tony's idea to mine. When Tony shares his vision, it seems as if he wants to boil the ocean. I believe that together we can make this work." As a start-up with very limited funds, we were not offering medical benefits. A few friends and family were standing with us and had invested enough funds to allow Sedera to survive its first year as a proof of concept. I didn't want others to risk any more money on these ideas until we had proven our ability to survive and demonstrated that our financial assumptions about the Sedera community worked in real life.

During our first year, while we grew from the two of us to six employees, our team had to rely on any existing coverage or services to handle our own medical costs. By the end of 2015, the community had grown from about 100 members from three businesses to closer to 300 members from the 15–20 small businesses that now comprised the Sedera community. As Jamie described it, it was now time for us to start eating our own dog food. We all agreed!

Jamie had been on a classic high-deductible individual plan that he had chosen while getting his previous company off the ground. Premium costs in 2015 were around $1,750 per month for the whole family, with a $5,000 per year deductible per family member. Jamie and Alisha then had two sons, with number three arriving on the scene a year later. Unfortunately, one of the boys was getting repeated ear infections. So, on top of the monthly premium cost of $1,750, they had to deal with doctor visit co-pays, prescription drug charges, and then when the condition demanded it, the price of putting in tubes for drainage of the inner ear. As the chart on the next page reveals, handling these charges during the first year of these inner ear infections cost $2,525 out of pocket.

Actually, the real charge for "protecting" their family that year was (annual premium cost [$1,750x12]) + ($2,525) = $23,525. All of that came out of pocket! If the premium cost had been largely picked up by an employer, it still would have been money that Jamie did not see in his paycheck. The comments I hear as I try to explain this concept always amaze me.

"Oh, but I love having such a small co-pay. I just pay $35 when I go to see my doctor." No, you don't. You pay the full year's premium cost before you have any access via your insurance plan. Then, on top of that, you pay the deductible and co-pays. Look at what this translated into for Jamie and his family in the chart that follows.

A family's one-year-old child had a persistent ear infection.
Here is a comparison of what this medical incident would have cost using health insurance with a $5,000 deductible vs medical cost sharing.

Health Insurance		Medical Cost Sharing
(Co-pay + RX) $60	Dr. Visit 1	$100 (Appt + RX)
(Co-pay + Shot) $135	Dr. Visit 2	$150 (Appt + Shot)
(Co-pay + RX) $60	Dr. Visit 3	$100 (Appt + RX)
(Co-pay + Shot) $135	Dr. Visit 4	$150 (Appt + Shot)
(Co-Pay) $35	Specialist	SHARED
$2,100	Surgery	SHARED
$2,525	Patient out-of-pocket + Annual Costs	$500
$21,000		$6,000
$23,525	Total	**$6,500**

The contrast between the two sides of this figure is striking. In 2015, under his existing health insurance, he had to pay $23,525 (annual premium cost of $21,000 plus the additional $2,525 for the ear infections) for healthcare. If he had stayed with this model, what actually happened in 2016 would have been financially crippling. In 2016, his son developed ear infections again because the tubes had fallen out. The whole deductible and co-pay business would have started all over again, with another year of $23,525 in bills or more. If he had already been on the medical cost-sharing model that Sedera provides, his 2016 costs would have been $6,500. The initial unshareable amount (IUA, as described in the figure) only applies once to any given medical incident. It is somewhat similar to the idea of a per-incident deductible. It is Sedera's approach to making sure that our members understand that we always need to have skin in the game. Even though these ear infections had persisted into a second year and would need a second surgical intervention to reinsert tubes, the first year's IUA would automatically cover that because it had already been applied to the same condition. As it was, because this was their first year on the plan, Jamie had to pay his $500 IUA out of pocket, with his employer, Sedera, handling the approximately $6,000 annual sharing amount for his family as a part of his salary. With Sedera only handling $6,000 of sharing costs for Jamie as an employee, this left another $17,500 for Sedera to be able to "share" with Jamie as a part of his salary! That's a nice wage increase.

In the previous chapter, we looked at why companies are usually tasked with paying some or all of the annual premium cost for health insurance plans. How much simpler it would be for this extra money just to go directly to the employee for them to make their own choices. But the realities of the antiquated tax code make employee empowerment challenging. In spite of these challenges, Jamie tells me that he and his family are saving around $17,000 a year since moving to the Sedera medical cost-sharing arrangement. That means that in the last four years, they have had an extra $68,000 in their pockets. What is not to like about that?

MY EXPERIENCE WITH MEDICAL BILLS

At the beginning of Sedera's second year, I had been a member of a Christian healthcare sharing ministry for almost 25 years. I loved these ministries and highly valued my experience working with them. But now was the time for my wife and me to stand directly with the Sedera community we were creating. We were blessed with good health but knew that at our ages we were taking a risk. We were now eligible for Medicare, but we wanted to join the rest of the team as a part of this grand experiment. So, we did.

In 2018, I began having prostate challenges and bladder stones. I knew I was responsible for directly paying for the doctor charges for the investigation of this condition as I did not have Medicare Part B, and I knew that Sedera would happily share anything above my initial unshareable amount ($500). But I soon came to understand that I would need to be admitted for a partial prostatectomy. As a hospital inpatient, Medicare would pay the bills for the surgery and the hospital. Now comes the crazy stuff.

On the day of the surgery, I arrived at the hospital very early, around 5 a.m., and the staff prepared me for the surgery. Thankfully, all went well. Around 4 p.m. that afternoon, the hospital advised me I was well enough to go home and promptly discharged me. Within a few hours of arriving home, it became impossible to pass urine, and I was in agony because of what we call acute retention. Being a doctor, I knew what was happening, but I hardly felt up to catheterizing myself. But severe discomfort and pain gives one the courage to do unpleasant things. It had probably been 40 years since I had catheterized a patient, but I was desperate, so I catheterized myself to release the urine and settled down for a rather unpleasant night. But the real unpleasantness came later when the bills arrived.

Because the hospital elected to send me home at the end of the day, rather than leaving me in the hospital overnight as previously planned, the hospital billed my surgery under a hospital outpatient code. This meant that Medicare was not responsible for paying for the procedure, and the hospital was billing me $18,000. Had they stuck to the original plan, keeping me in the hospital overnight and then billing Medicare, they could have only billed about $4,000. As a cash patient, they were billing me four and a half times as much as they would have been able to bill Medicare. This is wrong.

This type of billing and treatment is unconscionable. The hospital took advantage of me financially, while providing a lower level of care that did not include staying in the hospital overnight as planned. What makes matters worse, most patients wouldn't have any idea what to do in these circumstances. At least, as a subject matter expert, I knew how to fight the billing and get the hospital's agreement to accept the Medicare price for the procedure. But even this price was not "fair" to me. If they had kept me in the hospital overnight, Medicare would have paid the entire bill. Maybe I should have fought them to pay nothing, but I didn't feel that was appropriate, either. But I certainly became more "expert" following this personal experience.

Armed with this experience of what "inpatient" hospital care means in the bizarre world of insurance and Medicare, I was a little better prepared for the next assault on my urinary tract system: kidney stones, the worst pain I had ever experienced!

Almost a year after my prostatectomy, over the Thanksgiving weekend, I began to have trouble when kidney stones got caught between the kidney and the bladder. I won't frighten you with the details. Suffice it to say, I wouldn't wish this on my worst enemy. As Tim, my third-year resident ENT surgeon son, drove me to our nearby nonprofit hospital, I explained to him what I expected to experience when I arrived at the ER. What actually happened was even worse than I expected, but probably par for the course.

With pain so bad I could hardly think, my first port of call was the ER registration desk, where they asked me to pay $600 immediately by credit card to "cover the cost of the emergency room visit" and then asked me to sign some paperwork so that I could see the doctor. I explained to the clerk that every patient, by law, can receive emergency room treatment without paying anything up front or signing any paperwork. And the paperwork the hospital wanted me to sign would obligate me to pay "whatever the hospital chose to charge." I also told them that since I was of Medicare age, if they wanted me to sign that I would willingly pay the Medicare rate, I would be happy to do that. I asked the clerk to please document our conversation in the notes. The clerk agreed to register me under these conditions, and I was taken back to see the ER physician.

After a quick initial visit, the ER physician prescribed me an opioid to reduce the pain and said he would be back after a few minutes when I was feeling better. The pain relief was almost instantaneous, for which I was profoundly grateful. Ten minutes after receiving the injection, while on a delightful opioid high, the booking clerk returned to ask me to sign the hospital paperwork "in case I had to be admitted." Thankfully, I was still compos mentis enough to have warned my surgeon-in-training son that this second visit was likely. I just did not expect it so soon. I patiently explained again that no patient who had just been given an opioid painkiller is in any shape to provide "informed consent" for treatment. The full truth was that even if I were mentally sound to make such a decision, I would never sign any hospital paperwork committing me to paying whatever the hospital might choose to charge.

Soon, the doctor was back to arrange blood work and an X-ray because I looked dehydrated. The lab work showed evidence of dehydration and inflammation so severe that they decided to admit me overnight for rehydration and observation. My night was uneventful, but after the second dose of opioids, I asked that I only receive non-opioid medication to reduce the risk of dependence or addiction. Far too many patients become addicted when doctors prescribe opioids so freely, precisely because they are very effective. I didn't want to become part of that statistic. By lunch the following day, I was rehydrated, and the pain had eased. Yet another doctor came to see me to arrange for my discharge.

Following discharge, the billing fun began again. There were bills for everything you can imagine. So much for the $600 to cover the cost of the ER. There were bills from an ER doctor who worked for the hospital. But he belonged to a medical group owned by private equity funds who provide emergency rooms around the country with ER physicians. There were bills for another ER doctor. More bills for the X-ray. Bills for the lab work. Bills for the doctor who saw me to discharge me.

There was a nurse in the room when I was admitted who had heard much of my conversation with my son. As a budding surgeon, I wanted him to understand exactly what was happening with all of these people coming to see me and how each visit would impact the billing. The nurse came to see me shortly before I was discharged the next day. She wanted to let me know that what I was explaining to Tim about the hospital was true. Doctors and senior nurses got paid based on making sure that hospital beds were kept full, whether that was best for the patient or not. I learned in conversation with one of my doctors that whether or not Medicare would view my overnight stay as an inpatient admission depended on the billing code he used to explain my condition. When you can be admitted to a hospital but it may not be treated as an "admission" for insurance purposes, language really means nothing. George Orwell's *1984* describes this as "doublespeak."[1] Everything about the hospital admission system obscures the process and confounds the patient with relation to how costs are assigned and later collected. The hospitals, insurance companies, and private equity firms that control so many of the medical providers nowadays all benefit from the deliberate confusion around how medical bills will be assessed and collected. When I understood that this deception was deliberate, this was the moment that I said, "I must do something about this. After all, this hospital is part of a very large national Catholic charity that receives hundreds of millions of dollars in tax relief each year through the public purse."

Whether as individuals, small business owners, or those who control the healthcare expenses for hundreds or thousands of people, we have the opportunity to demand more transparency in medical spending and in medical billing practices. Each time any of us, as influencers, brings more business to the doctors and clinics driving medical cost transparency, we make it easier for others to join the movement. At some point, we will hit a tipping point when there is enough business for most physicians to move in this direction. However, these days it is still pretty challenging for doctors, unless they are born entrepreneurs, to manage the risks of opting out of the insurance system or succumbing to the corporate ownership of their practices. In the COVID-19 era, many smaller, independent practices have seen their revenues drop dramatically because so many patients put off regular doctor visits. For some of these physicians, the financial security of a local hospital offering to take over their practice is irresistible, even though they know they will now be forced to send all patients needing further care to that hospital. Helping doctors recapture their independence from the corporatization of medical care is a vital part of the process that I am describing.

Understanding the decision-making process is actually quite simple for those who are serious about cutting costs and improving access. If you choose to seek advice from anyone, make sure that it is from someone who is completely open with you about how they are being paid. From there, "starting with the end in mind" will likely lead to looking for an approach that rewards choices leading to a healthy lifestyle.

I'll close this chapter with one short comment from a broker here in Austin. Jason McKinley is one of a growing number of brokers who gets it when it comes to understanding the changes that we all need to make to improve our healthcare system. After serving both individuals and groups in his full-service agency, he has this to say:

I think the healthcare industry is broken. Everyone continues to get an increase in premium every year. Often the increase comes with a decreased amount of coverage. Business owners love Sedera. Again, with the cost savings that comes with it, the employees are the real winners. Sedera has worked for me and worked for my family. I like to say, 'Take the middleman out.' What Sedera has done for me and my family is trained us to shop for healthcare just as we shop for everything else. I think a lot of people are drawn to Sedera because of price. I don't like to sell on price, and I don't like it when people buy on price. Most of the time you get what you pay for. I do think, though, that Sedera has the best value, even though they are typically 30–50 percent less than what a business owner is already paying. I really haven't had a customer leave once they have tried Sedera. I've had a hard time finding a negative review about Sedera.

With comments like that, it is obvious that Jason is a good friend to Sedera and a good friend to me. But I include his comments because he has the passion that allows this movement to spread.

CHAPTER 10

A CALL TO ACTION

RECENTLY HAD BREAKFAST WITH A FRIEND and colleague here in Austin. Russell leads a local chapter of C12, a national association of CEO roundtables with chapters in most major cities across the country.[1] As we were wrapping up our conversation, he suddenly said to me, "Tony, through Sedera I've learned to be personally responsible for my health. I was hesitant to join at first, but I decided that I had to take action. Now, two and a half years later, my healthcare costs are less than half of what they used to be. I am not on any meds. I've lost 40 pounds. I am living proof of the value of your second opinion service, 2nd.MD. They saved me from an invasive nasal sinus operation, and in the process saved me about $5,000. Thank you for pushing me to be a part of the change that I needed to see to bring my own health under control."

William James, viewed by some as the father of American psychology, once said, "A new idea is first condemned as ridiculous and then dismissed as trivial, until finally it becomes what everybody knows." There is little that I have discussed in this book that is not already well known. Obviously, we cannot see the changes we want in healthcare until we are willing to look in the mirror and admit that the changes needed must begin with ourselves.

INNOVATION MEANS CHANGE

This progression from a ridiculous idea to a trivial fact to conventional wisdom is a natural consequence of the way all of us process new ideas. This progression has been true of so many of the ideas and innovations discussed in this book. Telemedicine was viewed as a new idea when doctors first began to experiment at scale with this approach 20 years ago. King Solomon was correct when he said, "Nothing under the sun is truly new."[2] My father did much of his work with his wealthier patients by telephone. Poor patients didn't have telephones in those days. We had to get back to the future, aided and abetted by the COVID-19 pandemic, to acknowledge what really should have been obvious for all to see: Telemedicine works, and works well, for patients and doctors in many situations. We don't need outsiders like the state medical society or bureaucrats somewhere to tell us that something we know is working fine "will not work" or does not fit into the boxes that they want to check off. I am fine with talking to a doctor by phone or video conference. I am happy to pay for a service if it is not included in my health plan. We are adults and can make those decisions for ourselves, thank you very much!

The same could be said of DPC medical practices, surgery centers, physician dispensing of medicines, or the absurdity of safe harbor laws that protect some organizations while making life impossible for others. Let the free market work its magic. Don't protect the middleman through unnecessary laws. If middlemen are producing value for the consumer, then the consumer will buy through them. If they don't provide value, why protect them in the first place? That is bad for everyone.

A concept in human behavior comes into play here. It is very hard to get someone to do something when their job and their livelihood depends on them not doing it. It used to be said in corporate IT departments that no one ever lost their job buying from IBM. What people meant by this remark was IBM was the safe choice because most people in information technology used IBM. Buying IBM in those days was not disturbing the status quo. In working with companies and individuals to help them understand the power of medical cost-sharing, again and again I have seen those responsible for benefits decisions stick with the safe decision. Previous experience dictated it was fine to switch from one insurance plan to another, but benefits managers felt they lacked the authority to switch from insurance to non-insurance. Even in the C-Suite, few senior executives are ready to admit that just tweaking the status quo is unlikely to accomplish much real improvement, and that even these incremental tweaks usually come at the expense of a decrease in efficiency in some other part of the plan. This is the "We can reduce your premium by 5 percent if you want, but this means that the deductible will need to jump from $2,500 to $4,000" type of example. This kind of slight reduction in the monthly premium paid by the company is actually offset by a much worse out-of-pocket situation for the employee.

We need to recognize that human behavior finds safety in stability. But innovation, dramatic improvement, nearly always implies significant change. That is why any call to action is a call to change. For change to happen, we need to lead. That is what leaders do. If you think back to Harris Rosen's impact on healthcare costs for the hotel and resort chain he started in Orlando, his ideas did not spring out of the incremental changes that his broker might have suggested. Harris fired his insurance company—and I suspect this meant firing the broker as well. In its place, he created his own plan.

ACTIONS SPEAK LOUDER THAN WORDS

This type of action begins with us, by starting with the end in mind. If my plan is to accomplish the three simple goals that I have described throughout this book as the foundation of a practical and achievable health plan, then I need to have those goals clearly in mind. Better access, with lower costs and measurably higher quality outcomes, is not going to happen spontaneously. But it can happen relatively easily if we are willing to embrace change. The existing insurance and broker world, reinforced by the decisions of politicians and medical policy think tanks, have tried to effect change from the top. But by equating "coverage" with "access," and leaving out the actual experience of the patient with the doctor, we have found ourselves adrift in a sea of experimental ideas not rooted in real patient experience or outcomes. It does not need to be this way.

The simple starting place, already shown to be overwhelmingly effective by nationwide movements such as direct primary care or by the incredible improvements to the health of the Alaskan Native population under the inspiration of the Alaskan Native Medical Center show us the path forward. Make access to quality primary care simple and based around a strong doctor-patient relationship. Let the doctor have the time to see their patients today, when the patient feels the need. Let the doctor and patient have the time they need to get to the heart of the problem. Let this access be already paid for so that there is no barrier to care. Build the relationship, and a lot of the care happens spontaneously. The mutual accountability and respect that come with this leads to dramatically better outcomes. Time for the doctor, focused on the patient, naturally leads to caring for mental health and physical health, not just handling the specifics of a current illness. By building in the convenience of modern access through calls, texts, and video conferencing, it is so much easier for both doctor and patient to communicate in a way that maximizes access and convenience, factors important to both parties, even while building deeper relationships.

Part of the magic that I am describing here is the cost reduction that just these simple steps already described will bring. Primary care is not expensive, as has been clearly demonstrated by the confluence of direct primary care with virtual primary care. Quality access, whenever it is needed, in the primary care setting keeps patients away from the expensive parts of the medical world except when such access is necessary. Who better to quarterback the patient through the medical system than a primary care doctor who knows the patient well? Who better to reassure the patient at ten o'clock at night when their child has a fever or unexpected rash? Who better to say, "This situation looks serious; let's meet at the clinic and I will go with you to the emergency room if need be." Now we have someone who understands the medical system helping make the decisions with the patient as to when they need to enter the much more expensive world of imaging and specialists and hospitalization. When this level of care is paired with the patient belonging to a medical cost-sharing community, such as Sedera, to deal with the expensive parts of the medical system, even the financial challenges are barely a concern.

It is absurd to think that we can ignore the lessons of the past 100 years and pretend that centralized, massive government systems work better than grassroots experimentation. Neither should we share the blindness of those who say they love free markets while turning a blind eye to the crony capitalism that is currently destroying people's faith in the American economic system, including healthcare. When the primary result of medical care appears to be taking as much of people's money as possible, something has gone seriously wrong.

Innovation comes out of experimentation and risk-taking by people who have skin in the game. When I started Sedera, I had already spent about one million dollars of my own money and almost two years of my time on research and development, legal, and regulatory issues. Unfortunately, ideas take time to develop.

I was running out of money and knew that if I wanted to prove that the concepts behind Sedera would work in the corporate environment, I had to find others who were convinced enough by these ideas that they would also invest their own money. By my estimate, we needed to raise an additional $400,000 to bring the Sedera concept to market. With the help of two very trusting friends who were ready to drop their existing jobs to join me in this grand adventure, we were able get Sedera off the ground. Of course, many others also played a part. But it is amazing what can be accomplished from a very small start by those who are fully committed to the end goal.

My friends and family who had the trust and the capacity to invest received what is known as a convertible note. They were being paid a reasonable interest rate for their loan, and one year later, Sedera would start paying their money back with interest, or, if my investors preferred, they could convert the debt into shares. Interestingly, not one person chose to take their money back. Everyone left their money with us, including the interest, which then converted into ownership in Sedera. That choice was a wise one for all concerned: a $10,000 investment in 2015 is worth more than $150,000 now.

Investments in early-stage companies are always risky. Usually, they are very risky. Many companies fail at this stage in their growth. Any investor willing to put their hard-earned money to work deserves both our best effort and our willingness to share in their risk to the maximum extent. I have made a point of investing in every round of fundraising so that I continue to have skin in the game in the same way as any new investor. This provides me with a reality check. Would I really invest in this company? If my answer is no, then why would I ever ask someone else to do so? That is just plain dishonest. Actions speak louder than words.

If you are going to ignite a movement, your actions matter. A movement to transform healthcare needs people in every part of the medical ecosystem to be willing to take action, whether it is investors who risk their capital, doctors who risk their medical practices, or brokers who are willing to step away from the drastic limitations of the existing health insurance system.

I have found that when you practice what you preach, people are more than willing to trust you. It takes a lifetime to build trust. Don't ever destroy that for a quick buck. Your word is your bond. Every time a broker knowingly provides a customer with a product that is not the best possible value just because the insurance company will pay them a higher commission than they would get with an alternate product, trust is being broken. With a passionate belief in the quality of a life well lived, you can establish trust with investors by being the same person in every part of your life. As the writer of the Psalms says of such people, they "keep their promises even when it hurts."[3]

SHARING IS NOT INSURANCE

Insurance is a contract by which a person or entity exchanges risk for monetary payment. An insurance contract can be enforced by law because it is a guarantee to pay on any risk that was assumed by the contract. This is why people can and sometimes should sue their insurance company if they feel the contract has not been honored. Litigation is another expense that insurance companies carry, increasing the cost of monthly premiums.

A medical cost-sharing community does not work on that premise. We voluntarily work on the principle that our word is our bond. Within the community, we believe that all members will give their monthly share. Community members choose to live healthy lifestyles. Each community member chooses to handle the small stuff, what we call our initial unshareable amount, out of our own pockets. We didn't join the community so that others can pay our small expected bills. Rather, we understand that all of us can share in each other's larger bills when those arise. This is a voluntary exchange rather than a contractual payment to take away risk. By sharing in each other's needs—by helping each member at their point of need—we gain the confidence to know that our own needs will be met when the time comes.

There are some important things to understand about the nature of a cost-sharing community such as Sedera. There is never a promise of payment. The promise, which we have rigidly adhered to from day one, is that anyone who has a medical need will have access to whatever funds are available to the community, as described in the community guidelines. We cannot guarantee funds because that would make us an insurance product. But we can promise that everyone will be treated fairly, as per the guidelines, and that our members will always have access to the community's available funds to help pay for their medical bills. When we were still in our earliest days as a company, before we had any real cash flow built up to handle medical needs as they arose, a friend and I set aside our own money to help cover any expenses for larger needs that might occur that couldn't be covered by the available community funds.

Sedera pays for community members' medical needs using funds that have been set aside by members for this purpose. Those funds are only ever used for this purpose or for actions that directly reduce the costs of members' bills. As such, we have an obligation to the community to make sure that members pay fair prices for those needs. There is no incentive for Sedera not to pay a medical need. Member money always remains the property of the members of the Sedera medical cost-sharing community. If there is more money in those funds than we reasonably assess as necessary to cover likely medical needs, then the money is returned to members in the form of lower monthly costs for shares.

Taking a clear and principled stand on these issues has helped the community gain the trust of its members in an amazing way. Six years into our operations, Sedera has helped the community pay every member bill that was submitted in accordance with our guidelines. The average time to pay these bills is about 14 days from when they are submitted. Community members, hospital providers, and clinics alike also know that Sedera will live by its word. I have sat in many of the Community Service Board meetings, where we discuss any member-submitted needs where there is a question as to whether the need meets the community guidelines. The board, which is composed of community members, invariably opts for bending over backward to help other community members if the guidelines allow that flexibility.

This is medical cost-sharing. It is not insurance, and it is not for everyone. If you don't trust other people, you should not join our medical cost-sharing community. If your word is your bond, we would love for you to be a part of our community. If you want to be a part of something that is larger than yourself and encourages you to be your best self, we welcome you. If your intention is to take rather than to give, you are going to be happier somewhere else. Again, actions speak louder than words.

When people of good will and shared principles choose to work alongside one another in a sharing community, medical cost-sharing offers a viable option. When those people choose to work with doctors and clinics, surgery centers, and hospitals that understand and value transparency and the cash-pay model, you have an ecosystem that is both cost-effective and moving toward sustainability.

People of action work in every part of the ecosystem I have described. These people have taken the risk to practice what they preach. Harris Rosen didn't just bemoan the unfair approach of the insurance companies looking after his staff. He fired them! Dr. Keith Smith didn't just complain about Medicare cutting his payments for anesthesia in complex cases to a ridiculously low rate. He fired them—even though this meant looking after Medicare patients at the hospital he was working for without billing for his services. When he opened the Surgery Center of Oklahoma, there was no guarantee that he could find patients willing to pay cash prices, even though the price was approximately one-third of the rate at other local hospitals. What did the patient care about cost when it was going to be paid for by the government or by their insurance company? Actions are costly, but in each of these cases, it turns out there is plenty of demand for better options.

Dr. John Hunt, Chief Medical Officer of the Sedera medical cost-sharing community, abandoned his successful academic career at the University of Virginia. He did so in protest against a top-down command/control structure that had evolved at an institution that had once been Jefferson's university. John's opinion was that the new powers at the university no longer cared about honest voluntary transactions, instead spending their days parasitizing the third-party payment system and coercing students into buying overpriced health insurance. John felt that the system was broken and irreparable, and so he left UVA in order to help build a new system. Actions speak louder than words.

Healthcare consumers also need to take action. One of my employees told me that the first month he and his wife sent in their monthly share, his wife was literally crying with joy that their money was going to help a person within the community, and not just sit in the coffers of some massive insurance company. A real person with a real name was getting their money because of the unexpected nature of their medical need. The ability to share gave my team member and his family great confidence that when they had a medical need, the community would respond in the same way toward them. And the cost was less than half of what they previously paid for health insurance. That was rather a nice feeling as well—and it is a clear part of our vision—to get people's health costs down so that their take-home pay goes up.

THE RISK OF INACTION

Individuals and companies can step up to the plate and take action. CEOs and other company staff have commented to me countless times about the risk they would be taking as a company to try a new way of handling their medical costs. What would their employees think about the changes? What happens if the community is unable to pay an employee bill? I don't usually reply what I am actually thinking: "So, what happens if you don't take any risk, if you yet again put off action? Then you get exactly the same result again as you have had in the past." Actions are what bring valuable change. No action, no changes!

The real risk is in inaction. No action pushes the country one step nearer a single-payer system administered from Washington, D.C., and a continuation of the crony capitalism that has created our dysfunctional health insurance companies, large hospital systems, and other large healthcare entities. We can all band together and show that there is a better way. Earlier, I talked about the vital importance of your Massively

Transformational Purpose. There are a variety of components to my MTP. Rescuing lower- to middle-income America from the stagnation of their wages over the past 20 to 30 years is one vital aspect of it. If the cost of medical premiums over the past 20 years had gone down in the way described, as they have for many of the companies detailed in this book, employee salaries could have increased by comparable amounts (assuming savings on healthcare are passed on to employees and not kept as retained earnings or given to executives as bonuses). An article in *Health Affairs* states as its title that "A decade of healthcare cost growth has wiped out real income gains for an average U.S. family."[4] Actually, three decades of medical cost growth has drowned out a generation of ordinary people's wage gains. We can right this wrong only if and when we take action. The action for company CEOs is to fire the existing system and put their healthcare dollars where the innovation and action is happening. Again, actions speak louder than words.

Trillions of dollars of economic growth should be in ordinary people's pockets. If the government saw the same savings in the medical programs it runs nationwide as it has seen at the Alaska Native Medical Center or we have seen in medical cost-sharing communities, our children and grandchildren would not have to pay tens of trillions of dollars in taxes to service the national debt. Massive problems, such as this, need a whole new way of thinking to challenge these unsustainable debts. Dealing with the excessive growth of medical spending is achievable. In the process, we can also improve access and quality of care. But each of us reading this book has to provide the actions that will bring this about.

Each of us can be a part of the answer. As a CEO, I can control my company's healthcare spending by demanding that we receive the quality, access, and lower costs that are there for the taking. Taking this "free money" involves some hard work and will involve a transition.

We begin by assuming power over our own healthcare choices and healthcare spending. Each of us must take the lead in those areas where we have the authority to take the lead. We can then share our successes with our peers and see the whole movement grow.

If there is any segment of society that needs to see the power of the free market at work, it is healthcare. This out-of-control medical corporate complex currently consumes one of every five dollars created in the wealthiest society the world has ever known. Healthcare costs can only be brought down to size if each decision maker, whether in a family, in an association, in a company, in a school district, in whatever groups you are a part of, actively chooses where and how they will spend their healthcare dollars. The government should not make these decisions for us. Since when has the government provided something more affordable in the area of healthcare? Government-mandated healthcare increasingly promotes the unrestrained choices of certain people who have learned that they can take the government's largesse for themselves at other people's expense. This is why the framers of the American experiment in independence and freedom established very clear and limited boundaries for what government should and should not be involved in.

THE POWER OF COMMUNITY

Limited government typically leads to human flourishing. Under a limited government, America flourished like no country before has ever seen. We should leave the decisions and risks of innovation in the hands of the people who choose to take such risks. With the risk comes the reward, or the loss if the risk does not work out. At its core, healthcare consumerism is about people taking responsibility for their choices, rather than relying on someone else to carry that responsibility for them. There is great power when we work with others who share our heart in dealing with these challenges. Community demonstrates the power of taking action together.

Consider how Uber and Lyft were able to mobilize the people of California to pass Proposition 22 in support of new, innovative models of work. *The New York Times* described this action: "The victory of Proposition 22, the most expensive initiative in the state's history, could help gig companies remake labor laws throughout the country."[5] This is literally the power of community to shape a nation's laws. But it takes action! Someone had to stand up and fight. Thank God for the free market that birthed both Uber and Lyft, both of which were financially able to stand up to the bully power of government that was trying to rob tens of thousands of people of a great way to support themselves while providing an incredible service to the community.

Like Uber and Lyft, which provide people with an opportunity to share assets like their time and an available vehicle, the medical cost-sharing community shares medical costs. This mutual exchange is viewed by both parties as a win-win exchange performed on a voluntary basis. Coercion in either example, a driver being forced to provide time and a vehicle against their will or a community member in medical sharing being forced to share a medical bill, implies one party does not feel they are getting value for money. In both cases, people will opt out of an exchange if they don't view it as genuinely valuable.

The concept of community is at the heart of the Sedera medical cost-sharing model. In a free environment, people are free to make choices that allow them to carry the challenges and the benefits of behaving as mature adults. We do not harm anyone else by committing to carrying responsibility for ourselves and our choices. When I make a choice to spend my own money to guarantee access to a direct primary care physician, how can anyone tell me that I cannot also enjoy the dramatic cost reduction in my overall medical care that comes with that choice?

Why would anyone want to penalize someone for making good choices? It makes no sense to disincentivize good choices while apparently promoting bad choices. Yet so often this is exactly what we see the country doing. Why should we penalize people for not having health insurance when many of those very people have made a perfectly rational choice to use the community medical cost-sharing model instead?

It is perfectly legitimate to assess a penalty when you make a choice that damages other people. If you choose to be a smoker, you know your health costs are likely to be a lot higher than other people's over the course of your lifetime. Although smoking primarily harms the smoker, the impact of secondary smoke on other people is also well-documented.[6] The market will naturally assign you a higher premium for your health insurance, in the same way that auto insurance will penalize you for having repeated accidents. Actions have consequences. Smokers are also penalized by high government taxes on cigarettes that go some of the way to covering the societal costs forced on us all by smokers.

The community relationship has two primary components: my relationship to the community, and the community's relationship to me. For these relationships to thrive, every community establishes guidelines that define the way members live and relate. Whether on the elementary school playground, the university tennis team, or in my medical practice, many situations have demanded of me some reciprocal rights and responsibilities. Rights do not come without responsibilities. Rights, by definition, relate to actions we take that have no automatic negative consequences on others. My right to liberty does not allow me to infringe on the liberties of others. Nor do others' liberties provide them the right to infringe on mine.

We see these same principles at work when dealing with healthcare costs. While the government should not force me into any one view of how I should pay for healthcare, my freedom to choose should not become a license to force others to take care of me when I don't bother to plan ahead. If I fall ill or have an accident needing major medical care, and I haven't bothered to have either health insurance or belong to a medical cost-sharing organization, then I need to carry the consequences of my choices. Of course, I should receive care at the time, but equally I should be totally responsible for paying for that care at a fair and reasonable rate afterward. Having neither insurance nor medical cost-sharing is irresponsible unless you have the financial capacity to handle large medical costs yourself. If you are wealthy enough to cover your own medical costs entirely, then you should be free to do so. This is the essence of self-insurance, whether for the individual or for a company. In this context, it is still wise to have some type of "stop loss" that will handle whatever you cannot handle. This is the classic understanding of the role of insurance. Insurance is just there to handle the catastrophic losses. Insurance handles your whole roof being damaged in a severe hailstorm, not the replacement of a few tiles because of some wind damage. Dealing with healthcare costs should follow similar basic economic principles.

Freedom to choose implies a maturity of character that is willing to take action and be personally responsible. This maturity of character is at the heart of the American way. In America, actions have always spoken louder than words. Whether it was taking the risk of fighting for liberty in the 18th century, having the courage to massively innovate during the 19th century, or fueling the spreading of free market economies and democratic principles in the 20th century, America has been a land of action. The same must be true in the 21st century. America is approaching the 250th anniversary of the Revolutionary War. It is time for ordinary people to preserve this great land's freedoms by choosing to take personal responsibility for personal actions. Healthcare is at the center of this challenge, because the healthcare payment system currently robs the ordinary person of the financial capacity to expand the American dream. There is a better way!

ACKNOWLEDGMENTS

I MAY HAVE STARTED SEDERA, but my son, Matt, who is now CEO of the first company I started, articulated some of its key concepts more than a decade earlier. Jamie Lagarde, Sedera's current CEO, joined me in the idea before the company was even formed. I knew it was going to take better folk than me to get such an important concept off the ground. John Oberg, who introduced me to Jamie, kindly agreed to be a part of the Sedera board before the company was ever formed. He stood by me as I imagined Sedera, researching what it would take to start the company. He staked not just his name and his reputation, but also some of his hard-earned money and several hours each week for the next year (around his full-time job) on turning this idea into a reality. We built a plan, hired our first dedicated employee (now our CEO), and waded into the fray. As such, John was a founding board member and true founder of the company with me.

I couldn't have done this without the team at Sedera—thank you for your love, your trust, and so much of your time. The earliest round of friends and family investors joined us at our risky point, when everyone thought we (and by extension, they) were mad. Thanks for helping to prove the naysayers wrong. Alisha Lagarde and Candy Rowen were willing to trust their husbands and stand with them in this adventure, and I thank them for that. Tom Rowen gave up the security of his management position with a large insurance company to share his expertise and keep Sedera on the good side of the law. The leadership of C12 stood with us in believing that this idea was important enough that they would risk their reputation and the standing of C12 to help see this become a reality. David Underwood told me he and his company would join Sedera even before we had named or formed the company.

Jenny Aghamalian, Sedera's Chief Strategy Officer, and Bob Greenlee of Tusk Strategies navigated me through the complexities of writing and bringing this book to market. My editor Darren Thornberry and my son Jon brought focus and clarity (and brevity!) to the final manuscript. Allen Arnold managed the completion of this project and brought it in for a landing.

USEFUL ORGANIZATIONS & SOURCES FOR NEXT STEPS

A useful one-stop shop for information about all of the following is the Sedera website at www.sedera.com or you can call the Sedera team at 855-293-3915.

FOR MORE DETAILED INFORMATION ABOUT
Tony Dale's Personal Website
- www.tonydale.com

Direct Primary|Patient Care
- www.d4pcfoundation.org
- www.atlas.md
- www.hint.com
- www.sedera.com/directcaremap

The Growing Free Market Medical Movements
- www.fmma.org
- www.healthcareforyou.com
- www.physiciansforreform.org
- www.aapsonline.org

Understanding Pharmacy Benefit Managers (PBMs)
- www.aapsonline.org/safe-kickbacks-inflate-costs-cause-drug-shortages

Other Questions or Concerns
- Contact Public Affairs at Sedera
    Email: press@sedera.com
    Website: www.sedera.com/press-room

NOTES

PREFACE

1. athenahealth, "Expert Forum: The rise (and rise) of the healthcare administrator," November 7, 2017, https://www.athenahealth.com/knowledge-hub/practice-management/expert-forum-rise-and-rise-healthcare-administrator.

CHAPTER 1

1. Felicity and I both trained as doctors at the world-famous Royal and Ancient Hospital of St. Bartholomew, or Barts as it is affectionately known by all. Barts, established in 1123, soon celebrates its 900th birthday.

2. See Tony Rao, "Five things doctors should know about the 1975 junior doctors' strike," *BMJ* 2015, 351:h6155, doi: https://doi.org/10.1136/bmj.h6155.

3. Isaiah 42:8, New Living Translation.

4. James 4:6, New Living Translation.

5. Ephesians 2:8–10, New Living Translation.

6. See www.tonydale.com.

7. Lee Kurisko, *Health Reform: The End of the American Revolution?* (Saint Paul, Minnesota, Alethos Press, 2009), pp. 9, 10, 11, 15, 16, 19.

8. https://www.bloomberg.com/news/articles/2019-07-05/harris-keeps-tripping-up-on-her-medicare-for-all-fuzziness

9. Lee Kurisko, *Health Reform: The End of the American Revolution?* (Saint Paul, Minnesota, Alethos, 2009), p. 22.

10. Lee Kurisko, *Health Reform: The End of the American Revolution?* (Saint Paul, Minnesota, Alethos, 2009), p. 26.

11. Lee Kurisko, *Health Reform: The End of the American Revolution?* (Saint Paul, Minnesota, Alethos Press, 2011), pp. 74–75.

CHAPTER 2

1. Marty Makary, *The Price We Pay* (New York: Bloomsbury Publishing, October 2019). Dr. Makary is a professor of health policy and management at the Johns Hopkins Bloomberg School of Public Health.

2. Ephesians 5:11, New International Version.

CHAPTER 3

1. C.L. Gray, *The Battle for America's Soul* (New Hickory, North Carolina, Eventide Publishing, 2011).

2. W.J. Korab-Karpowicz, "Plato: Political Philosophy," s.v. "5. The Government of Philosopher Rulers, Internet Encyclopedia of Philosophy, https://iep.utm.edu/platopol/#H4, March 2, 2021. Copied from https://en.wikipedia.org/wiki/Plato%27s_political_ philosophy.

3. Robin Waterfield, editor and translator, *Plato, Republic*, (Oxford, Oxford University Press, 1998), p. 111, quoted in C.L. Gray, *The Battle for America's Soul (*New Hickory, North Carolina, Eventide Publishing, 2011), p. 37.

4. Betsy McCaughey, "Obama's Health Rationer-in-Chief," *Wall Street Journal,* August 27, 2009, https://www.wsj.com/articles/SB1000 14240529702037066045743744632800098676. Journal of the American Medical Association, June 18, 2008.

5. Lee Kurisko, *Health Reform: The End of the American Revolution?* (Saint Paul, Minnesota, Alethos, 2009).

6. Betsy McCaughey, "Obama's Health Rationer-in-Chief," Wall Street Journal, August 27, 2009, https://www.wsj.com/articles/SB 10001424052970203706604574374463280009867. Journal of the American Medical Association, June 18, 2008.

7. Michel Accad, *Moving Mountains: A Socratic Challenge to the Theory and Practice of Population Medicine* (Green Publishing House, 2017), https://movingmountainsthebook.com.

CHAPTER 4

1. Emma Lazarus, "The New Colossus," November 2, 1883, National Park Service, https://www.nps.gov/stli/learn/historyculture/colossus.htm.

2. https://urbanpolicy.berkeley.edu/pdf/Ch2Blank0404.pdf

3. Acts 4:34, New Living Translation.

4. The first of these cases involved Christian Care Ministry's Medi-Share, one of the earliest and largest of the groups exempted by the Affordable Care Act. The Kentucky Department of Insurance had been skirmishing with Medi-Share since 2002, when it first filed complaints that Medi-Share looked too much like an insurance plan and, as such, needed to file within the state as an insurance plan. By 2010, the case known as Kentucky v. Reinhold came before the Kentucky Supreme Court. The court concluded, in a divided opinion, "that the Medi-Share program does provide a 'contract for insurance.'" But this was not the end of the case. By 2012, Medi-Share was facing closure in Kentucky, even while various groups were actively calling for state legislation to exempt Medi-Share from insurance department regulations using "safe-harbor" rules. As of June 2013, the court ruled that Medi-Share could operate in Kentucky because Medi-Share had changed its system of paying medical bills to bring it into conformity with state regulations. The second of these cases involved a smaller Christian healthcare sharing ministry in Idaho known as Altrua. In these cases, the ministries are challenged for some portion of their plan which is thought to be "proof" that they are operating as an illegal insurance scheme. The language used implies that if something "looks like a duck and quacks like a duck, then it must be a duck." But regulatory matters aren't that simple. This time, the Idaho Supreme Court sided with Altrua in a 2013 (5-0) ruling stating that Altrua was not an insurance company.

5. Galatians 6:10, New International Version.

6. Ephesians 3:20, New International Version.

CHAPTER 5

1. Rebecca Pifer, "CBO finds COVID-19 puts Medicare trust fund insolvency just 4 years away," *HealthCareDive*, September 4, 2020, https://www.healthcaredive.com/news/cbo-finds-covid-19-puts-medicare-trust-fund-insolvency-just-4-years-away/584725/.

2. Timothy Snyder, "What Ails America," *The New York Review*, September 3, 2020, https://www.nybooks.com/daily/2020/09/03/what-ails-america/.

CHAPTER 6

1. *Hospitalist* is a term used for doctors who specialize in the care of patients in the hospital. Just like a family doctor oversees your care outside of the hospital, the hospitalist is the person overseeing your care within the hospital.

CHAPTER 7

1. See https://www.rosencare.com/.

2. Lizette Alvarez, "One Man's Millions Turn a Community in Florida Around," *New York Times*, May 25, 2015, https://www.nytimes.com/2015/05/26/us/tangelo-park-orlando-florida.html.

3. Ayla Ellison, "Former Haven CEO Dr. Atul Gawande on what went wrong for the healthcare venture," *Becker's Hospital Review* (February 26, 2021). https://www.beckershospitalreview.com/strategy/former-haven-ceo-dr-atul-gawande-on-what-went-wrong-for-the-healthcare-venture.html.

4. The Burden of Medical Debt: Results from the Kaiser Family Foundation/New York Times Medical Bills Survey," January 2016. Prepared by Liz Hamel, Mira Norton, Karen Pollitz, Larry Levitt, Gary Claxton and Mollyann Brodie, Kaiser Family Foundation

CHAPTER 8

1. Leo Tolstoy, "Three Methods of Reform," in *Pamphlets* (Essex, UK, Free Age Press, 1900), p. 29, https://www.google.com/books/edition/Pamphlets_Translated_from_the_Russian/kVBYAAAAMAAJ?hl=en&gbpv=0.

2. C.L. Gray, *The Battle for America's Soul* (New Hickory, North Carolina, Eventide Publishing, 2011).

3. https://www.physiciansforreform.org/fix

4. Karen Pollitz, "High-Risk Pools for Uninsurable Individuals," KFF, February 22, 2017, https://www.kff.org/health-reform/issue-brief/high-risk-pools-for-uninsurable-individuals/.

5. Douglas Eby—Consilium Southcentral Foundation Nuka System of Care (Alaska)— Vårdmaktpodden, podcast, https://vardmaktpodden.podbean.com/e/34-douglas-eby-consilium-south-central-foundation-nuke-system-of-care-alaska-vardmaktpodden/.

6. Elaina George, *Big Medicine: The Cost of Corporate Control and How Doctors and Patients Working Together Can Rebuild a Better System* (Saint Paul, Minnesota, Alethos Press, 2015), kindle version Chapter 9, location #664.

CHAPTER 9

1. George Orwell, *1984* (New York: Harcourt, Inc., 1979).

CHAPTER 10

1. See https://www.c12group.com/ for more information on this remarkable movement of CEOs.

2. Ecclesiastes 1:9, New Living Translation.

3. Psalm 15:4, New Living Translation.

4. David I. Auerbach and Arthur L. Kellermann, "A Decade of Health Care Cost Growth Has Wiped Out Real Income Gains for an Average US Family," *Health Affairs* vol. 30, no. 9, September 2011, https://www.healthaffairs.org/doi/full/10.1377/hlthaff.2011.0585.

5. Kate Conger, "Uber and Lyft Drivers in California Will Remain Contractors," *New York Times*, November 4, 2020. https://www.nytimes.com/2020/11/04/technology/california-uber-lyft-prop-22.html.

6. See Centers for Disease Control and Prevention, "Smoking & Tobacco Use: Secondhand Smoke (SHS) Facts," January 5, 2021. https://www.cdc.gov/tobacco/data_statistics/fact_sheets/secondhand_smoke/general_facts/index.htm.

ABOUT THE AUTHOR

Tony Dale is committed to changing healthcare for the better. As founder and chairman of The Karis Group and Sedera, Tony has directly impacted the lives of millions of patients seeking the best possible care at fair and affordable prices.

His interest in tackling the business side of healthcare began following his rude introduction to the American medical system when he injured his knee playing basketball and needed knee surgery. After being quoted an initial price, then receiving a significantly larger bill, Tony was determined to find a way to help people find better access to quality and affordable care.

Tony founded The Karis Group in 1996 to help patients negotiate their exorbitant medical bills. Since then, the Karis Group has expanded and been acquired by Point Health, and the group now supports over a million members with healthcare navigation and bill negotiation before, during, and after a healthcare event.

In 2014, recognizing the unmet needs in the traditional health insurance industry, Tony founded Sedera as an alternative medical cost-sharing solution. Medical cost-sharing allows members to be part of an organized community to share funds for medical care. Today, Sedera offers services all across America, to groups large and small, helping both employees and individuals deal with their larger medical costs through the Sedera medical cost-sharing community.

Before moving to the United States in 1987, Tony practiced family medicine in London's East End and helped found Caring Professions Concern, subsequently known as Christians in the Caring Professions. Tony and Felicity Dale, both family doctors, trained at St. Bartholomew's Hospital, London. They now live in Austin, Texas, surrounded by four children, eleven grandchildren, and a dog and a cat.

Made in the USA
Las Vegas, NV
10 July 2021